Sinks of London L:

CH00642425

George Cruikshank

Alpha Editions

This edition published in 2023

ISBN : 9789357939935

Design and Setting By
Alpha Editions
www.alphaedis.com
Email - info@alphaedis.com

Contents

CHAPTER I.

COMMON LODGING HOUSES, CADGERS, &c., &c.

THESE two subjects are, perhaps now the only ones remaining, in what is termed the "walks of life," of which a correct description has not yet been given. All the old topics, such as the beauties of the country, and the ancient stories of love and heroism, which have afforded so much employment to the pencil, the muse, and the worker-up of novels, have long been considered as the beaten track; and the relaters of fiction, at least those who lay claim to any thing like originality, have been fain to leave the romantic path, with its old castles and wondrous deeds, and so forth, and seek for heroes behind a counter, amidst the common-place details of business, and for scenes amongst the intricate windings of lanes and alleys. In short, novelty is the grand charm for this novel-writing age.

Independent of the hosts of "Military and Naval Sketches of Mr. Such-a-one," "the Author of So-and-So's Reminiscences," &c., with the usual abundance of matter, that daily crowd from the press, we may notice amongst the really useful works that have lately appeared, the "Old Bailey Experience," "Essays on the Condition of the People," "the Dishonest Practices of Household Servants," and "the Machinery of Crime in England, or the Connection between the Thieves and Flash Houses;" but, valuable as these articles are, and they are certainly of some importance to society, has there any one, we might ask, ever entered into the Common Lodging House,—the Vagabond's Home,—a place that abounds in character and crime? The only information which we have had in these dens of poverty and vice, has been merely through the Police Reports, when some unfortunate defaulter had been taken out of one of those skulking-holes. On such occasions we are told, amongst the usual remarks, that the accommodation in those houses were exceedingly cheap, and that the lodgers herded together indiscriminately, &c.; but how such houses were really conducted, and of the manners and characters of most of the people who frequented them, the public may be said to be almost in perfect ignorance. In like manner with that fraternity called "Cadgers," our knowledge has been equally limited. No correct account has ever yet been given of this idle, but cunning class of the community. All that we have been told concerning them, is, to use the common phrase, but mere hearsay. We remember reading, some few years ago, of one of those begging gentry boasting of being able to make five shillings a day. He considered that sixty streets were easily got through, from sunrise to sunset, and that it was strange indeed if he could not collect a penny in every street.

Now, this very same anecdote we read, not many days since, in a new work, entitled, "A History of the Working Classes," as something, of course, just brought to light.

The story, too, in that by-gone piece of notoriety, "Pierce Egan's Life in London," about the beggar's opera, where the lame and the blind, and other disordered individuals, were said to meet nightly, in a place called the "back slums," to throw off their infirmities, and laugh at the credulity of the public, was, not a great many weeks ago, trumped up into a paragraph in one of our weekly journals as a fact just discovered, and the curious were referred to a certain house in St. Giles's, in corroboration thereof. Indeed, we think it would be easy to prove that what little is known of the Common Lodging House, and those people the Cadgers, is neither more nor less than mere reports, and which like the generality of reports, contain not always the truth.

It certainly appears strange that those two subjects, which offer such an abundance of original matter to writers and other observers of mankind, should have remained so long without any other notice than merely that they were known to exist. Seemingly strange, however, as this singularity is, sufficient reasons, perhaps, may be given for it. There can be little doubt, at least there is none in our mind, that since the commencement of the *Spectator* and *Tatler*, periodicals have principally assisted in developing, if we may so term it, the powers of observation. Intelligent readers of this kind of literature would naturally turn away from the insipid stuff of the rhymer, and the equally sentimental trash of the getter-up of fiction, of which our old magazines were mostly composed, to the more rational parts of the publication, such as original essays, critiques, stories which had really some truth for their foundation, or any thing which bore the stamp of newness. This secret of attraction would, of course, soon be found out, by those most interested in the sale; but the grand introduction of utility was at that period when the *Waverley* novels made their appearance. Then, instead of the exaggerated imaginings of a diseased brain, with all its superhuman agency, we had History beautifully blended with Fiction, or rather Truth, accurate descriptions of nature, and correct pictures of life, both high and low. We all remember what powerful sensations those literary wonders at first created, and what a crowd of imitators followed in their train. The Magazines soon caught up the tone, and became doubly interesting, with the lives of private soldiers, "Two or Three Years in the Peninsula," and the "Subaltern." The camp and the man-of-war now poured forth their vast stories of anecdote and adventure, in all shapes and sizes—octavo and article—sketches of character, local customs and antiquities, filled up the other attractions of the day; and to read for improvement, while we read for amusement, was almost considered the fashionable employment of time.

These excellent topics, doubtless, had their season, and when done, our wholesale dealers in wisdom, the Publishers, well knew that their great patron, the public, would not be content with what had gone before. Something was to be again produced, that would make the press move; and that something, we believe, every one will agree with us, that, notwithstanding the splendour of Genius which the imaginative tribe are endowed with in this mental age, was to be that which was *new*—that, in fact, which would *sell*. This, as might be expected, caused the booksellers and their hacks to look around them, and the tempting gilt which the former held out, (scanty though the quantity always be!) was yet too keen a spur to the flagging wits of hungry scribblers, to allow them to lie idle. Society was once more ransacked, and that which formerly gave pleasure was now found to be too old for entertainment. Bad practices were discovered to exist amongst those with whom honesty was thought to dwell—the seat of justice was found to be but the seat of corruption—and so high in repute had Unions risen in the land, that they even extended to the very pests of society—the men who lived by plunder. It is to this desire for change, then, that we are indebted for those admirable novels of the French writer Paul de Kock, which have lately appeared; and wherein are portrayed, with such faithfulness, the plodding manners and steady characters of shop-keepers, instead of the high-toned conversation of polished society or the homely but innocent simplicities of a country life— that old ground-work of fiction. The same may be said of those "Essays on the Condition of the People,"—"Household Servants,"—the "Old Bailey Experience," and those equally instructive articles on the "Machinery of Crime in England, or the Connection between the Thieves and the Flash Houses," which all owe their origin to the same cause. It therefore can scarcely excite surprise that the Common Lodging House and Cadger should have remained so long without notice, when, if we take but a little time to reflect, we shall easily perceive that this work of observation is but just now going on, and that the very period in which we now live, is what with justice may be called but—the Age of Inquiry.

The Common Lodging House, as the reader no doubt understands, is a house of accommodation for all classes—no matter what may be their appearance or character—only provided that they can procure, when required, the necessary quantity of coins. In every considerable village in the kingdom there is a lodging-place called the "Beggars' House;" and in every town, more or less, according to its size or population. In London there are hundreds and thousands of houses of this description, from the poor tenant of a room or cellar, with its two or three shake-down-beds upon the floor, to the more substantial landlord with his ten or twenty houses, and two or three hundred beds. Among these the houseless wanderer may find shelter, from a penny to three halfpence, twopence, threepence, fourpence, and sixpence a night, on beds of iron, wood, and straw, or on that more lofty couch a hammock; and some (that is, the penny-a-night lodger) have often no softer resting place than the hard floor. This common lodging-house business is a thriving trade; only small capital is required, for an old house will do, no matter how the rain beats in, or the wind whistles through, in a back street or filthy lane, for the more wretched the neighbourhood, the better; old bedsteads and beds, clothes of the coarsest description, with a few forms, and a table or so, for the kitchen, are all that is necessary for the concern. The front room, or what is usually termed the parlour, is generally fitted up into a shop, or, when this is not the case, there is always some accommodating neighbour, who has the following articles for sale: viz., bacon, butter, cheese, bread, tea, coffee, sugar, tobacco, potatoes, red and salt herrings, smuggled liquors, and table-beer. Some add the savoury profession of the cook to that of the huckster, and dish up a little roast and boiled beef, mutton, pork, vegetables, &c. The whole of these, the reader may be assured, are of a very moderate quality: they are retailed to the lodgers at very profitable prices, and in the smallest quantities, such as a halfpenny worth of butter, bacon, cheese, tea, coffee, sugar, tobacco, &c.; and, for the trifling sum of one penny, the poor epicure may gratify his palate with a taste of beef, mutton, and so on. Very little credit is given in those creditable places, and that only to those who are well-known; they who have not that advantage, often are compelled to take the handkerchief off their necks, the coat, and even the very skirts off their backs, to give to the cautious housekeeper, before they can procure a night's lodging, or a morsel of food; indeed, in the country, it is a common thing, when a traveller (which is the respectable appellation by which the alms-seeking gentry designate themselves) seeks for a night's lodging, for the landlord to refuse admittance, unless the applicant carries a bundle, which is looked upon as a kind of security, should he not have the desirable in his pocket.

It may naturally be supposed that, where there are such little outlays and such large returns, that good round sums must be produced; indeed, there are few who commence this kind of life, but soon secure to themselves an independency. There are many whom we could mention, who have accumulated such large fortunes by the encouragement of vagrancy, as now to be the proprietors of vast property in houses, and who still carry on large establishments by means of deputies, and in their deputies' names, while they themselves live in fashionable style on the borders of the town. The servants that are kept in those houses are in general men, they being considered better adapted to keep peace and quietness than women. It is customary with lodgers, who have anything of value, to deposit it with the landlord, and, in most cases, it is returned with safety. There are some whose character stands so high for honesty, that twenty pounds and upwards may be entrusted with them; but there are those again with whom it would not be prudent to leave a rag, and who often colleague with ruffians to get up a row during the night, to rob the lodgers, they of course coming in for a share of the booty. It is true, too, that in a great many of those houses men and women scorn all restraint, and hate any thing in the shape of a barrier. As regards cleanliness very little can be said for any; they all abound, more or less, with those small creeping things, which are said to be so prolific on the other side of the Tweed, and in the *dear country*. To delineate, however, the characters of the different houses, comes not at present within our limits; that of itself would fill volumes with the most extraordinary interest; and what then would be the descriptions of the crowds who frequent such houses—the thousands and tens of thousands who exist in this country by what is called their wits—whose trade is imposture, and whose whole life one continued exercise of the intellects? The flash letter-writer and the crawling supplicant; the pretended tradesmen, who live luxuriously on the tales of others, and the real claimant of charity, whose honest shame will hardly allow him to beg for sufficient to procure the hard comforts of a bed of straw; the match seller and ballad-singer, whose convenient profession unite the four lucrative callings of begging, selling, singing, and stealing; gangs of shipwrecked sailors, or rather, fellows whose iron constitutions enable them for the sake of sympathy, to endure the most inclement weather, in almost a state of nudity, and among them only one perhaps ever heard the roar of the ocean; jugglers, coiners, tramps (mechanics seeking work), strolling players, with all the hangers-on of fairs, races, assizes, stable-yards; besides the hosts of Irish who yearly migrate from sweet Erin to happy England, to beg, labour, and steal. Here then, is a wide field for speculation, a vast common in life, where a character may be almost picked up at every step—mines of vice and misery as yet unexplored. A road that has never yet been trodden by the man of the pen, and very rarely by him of the pencil. If a few straggling mendicants, or some solitary wretch, have occasionally been sketched, the great centre of the sons of Cain—the outcast's home—has never yet been entered; that place has remained sacred to the tell-tale eye of each observer. But enough of this: we will now enter among these new scenes, and in order to give a correct view of the ways and doings of this strange life, will at once introduce the reader to the head-quarters of the cadgers—St. Giles's.

CHAPTER II.

ST. GILES'S—THE CADGER'S HEAD-QUARTERS.

THE house, or rather establishment (for it contains no less than eight houses, having a moderate-sized court within its boundary, in which stands a large gas lamp) to which we intend to conduct the reader, is situate at No. 13, —— Street, St. Giles's. The proprietor being what is called a gentleman—a man of property—and, like all men of property, of course, wishes not to have his name mentioned but in a respectable way—we therefore, with all respect for the power of wealth, will accommodate him with a dash.

This cavern was opened some forty years ago, by a man of the name of — —, a native of that cautious country, *"Canny, tak care o' yoursel."* The Scotchman, with the characteristic foresight of his countrymen, soon saw that to set up prudence in the midst of wanton waste, was a sure and ready way to accumulate the *bawbees*. Accordingly, he took a shop and house at the aforesaid number, and commenced giving shelter to the wild and the profligate. Trade thrived, and, ere long, Sawney had reason to bless the day he crossed the border. He not only grew a rich but a *braw* man—put his sons to respectable professions, and expended as much in setting them up in the world, as might have made them no common lairds in the land of thistles, and finally gave up the ghost, breathing his last breath amidst the air of plenty, leaving his money-making craft to his eldest son, who still carries on this establishment, as well as two others, one in the Broadway, St. Giles's, and the other in Long Acre, through the means of a deputy, and in the deputy's name, while he himself takes his ease in elegant style, a little way out of town, and is reputed to be the possessor of a great number of houses besides.

This grand cadging rendezvous, then, is under the superintendence of a deputy, and is kept up in his name; he is assisted by his wife and under deputy (men-servants), and a few female domestics. This man—that is, the leader of the band—hails we believe from Cambridgeshire. He is of a slight make, with a shrewd cast of the eye. Formerly he figured in a gentleman's family, and has still much of the air and dress of a lackey: he is nevertheless well adapted for his situation; is affable and free, gambles, and is the companion of the lodgers in the house, but knows them not in the street. When any of the inmates chance to meet him in one of their alms-seeking rambles, and present their hat, to see if he will set an example to unwilling people, he never drops in more than one poor penny; his wife, however, is considered a trump (a generous woman), and never has the collection-box held to her, but invariably lets fall a *tanner*, to shew that she is a *Gemman's* wife. These people have the reputation of being honest: anything intrusted to them, of whatever value, is certain of being returned. Robbery and petty thefts are here very rare, and fights are never allowed in the house, if the landlord is at home. There are two kitchens, one for the males and the other for the females: the men are not permitted to visit the women, and, until after eleven at night, the time the women's kitchen is cleared, very few of the latter are allowed to disturb their masculine neighbours; those who have that privilege, are the select few, who are pleased to term themselves *wives*. There are sleeping apartments, too, for the different sexes, and rooms for those who pass as married people; and when any of the fair part of the inmates happen, in their perambulations, to meet with a friend of the opposite gender, and find, as they sometimes do, that it will be necessary to have a little private communion before they part, the landlord has so far sympathized with such persons, as to provide a room or two for their particular use. In short, this place, besides being a common lodging house, adds to it that now very necessary convenience—a brothel.

There are considerably more than one hundred beds in this house, made of wood and iron, distributed three and six in a room; the single ones are fourpence, and the double ones sixpence; and when we add the profits of this to that of the other two establishments, it must be allowed that the whole must amount to a gentlemanlike sum.

It is now our duty to enter this abode; and though accustomed to those retreats of vice and crime, we actually did pay a visit to this very house, one Saturday evening, and there remained until Monday morning, taking, from first to last, careful notes of the most extraordinary characters and their ways, in order that our first sketch might be a correct picture of the manner in which these outcasts of society spend the last, the best, and the first part of the week.

Well, then, on Saturday afternoon, upon a certain day, we directed our steps to that well known spot of this mighty part of the world—the Rookery, the appropriate title given to that modern Sodom, St. Giles's. On entering this region of sin, we, of course, had the usual difficulties of foot-passengers to encounter, in picking and choosing our way among the small but rich dung heaps—the flowing channels and those pitfalls, the cellers, which lie gaping open, like so many man-traps, ready to catch the unwary traveller. At length, however, we reached No. 13, —— Street, which was pointed out to us by a damsel standing in one of the many groups which are usually collected there, discussing the queries of that city, as being the habitation that we were in search of.

CHAPTER III.

THE CADGING HOUSE.

AS this is the first attempt that has been made to describe a Cadging House, we perhaps may be excused in being somewhat particular. The outside of this dwelling was more cleanly and decent than we had been led to expect. The window of the low front room, which was large and rather bowed, still retained the remains of its former shop-like appearance, was modestly screened in the inside by a green curtain; and the step of the door was nicely scoured and sanded.

On entering, we were struck with the establishment-like appearance of the room. Rows of common tin tea-pots were ranged along the dresser. As for the shelves, they literally lined the walls, well filled with plates, dishes, and tea-ware. The landlady came forward to meet us, a tall, genteel woman, with the manners of one apparently used to better society. After putting down our groat, and giving into her hand a certain garment wrapped in a handkerchief, in case of accidents, we were told that the men's kitchen was in the next house, the first door on the right hand side, in the entry. By this, we found that the threshold on which we then stood, was no less than the high quarters set apart for the barrack-master himself. Accordingly, we sallied out for No. 12: but, before going in, we took the liberty to make a survey of this "Vagabond's Home!" and, in troth, it did well deserve that name.

The low front room or parlour, whose fate it was now to be the Cadger's Kitchen, had certainly the same shop-like appearance as that of No. 13—but there the likeness ended. The door, which led into the street, instead of having the clean, welcome, and open look of its neighbour, was fast nailed up, and bore evident marks that many a sick man had leaned against it. The door-light—the window above the door—had been taken out, or what is more likely, knocked out, and its place supplied with a wooden shutter, which was raised up during the day, to let in the light, and air: and as for the window itself, with the exception of a few panes of glass in the centre, here and there patched with brown paper, it was almost wholly made up with squares of wood—giving ocular proof that glass was of a very brittle nature in St. Giles's.

After satisfying ourselves thus far, we proceeded to explore the interior. A narrow passage ran between the houses, and led into a tolerably large court, which, with those two, contained the number of houses already stated. At the foot of this entry stood two or three Moll Flanders looking husseys, who, it may be supposed, did not neglect a passing salute. Farther up the yard, were some half-dozen fellows, in parti-coloured dresses, (and not over particular about shoes and stockings) smoking their cutties, and gambling at pitch-penny.

We next proceeded to the kitchen—and a den-like retreat it was—dark and gloomy from the partial light let in by the few remnants of glass, it seemed well calculated to harbour felon thoughts. The room itself was moderate enough in size—a good fire, and an excellent grate, containing a copper of boiling water, always kept full by a pipe conveyed to it from a cask raised on one side of the fire-place, was all that we could see that approached to anything like luxury or comfort. Beneath this cask lay a heap of coke and coal, and a coal-heaver's shovel leaned against the wall, at the service of any one who loved a cheerful hearth. The floor and walls did not differ much in colour, the former being of a dusky hue, that knew of no other purifier save the birchen broom; and the latter, a dirty red—a daub long since and clumsily made. A cuckoo-clock ticked on one side of an old cupboard, and before the window was spread a large deal table, at which sat the landlord playing at cards with a couple of ruffian-like fellows. A small table (whose old-fashioned, crooked, mahogany legs, showed that it had once been in a more honoured place; but the rough deal covering with which it had been repaired, denoted that it was now only fit for *cadger's plate*)—stood at the other end of the room, behind the door. A man, in a decent but faded suit of clothes, sat on one side—his arms were stretched over the table, and his head half-buried within them—he was, apparently, asleep. The white apron, that was wrapped round his waist, clearly proclaimed to what class he belonged—the "Begging Tradesmen." A few things, tied to a blue handkerchief, rested on one side of his head; and a parcel of ballads, his whole stock-in-trade, lay on the other. Before the fire, warming his back, stood a short, thick-set man, humming the air of a vulgar ditty; his hands were thrust into the pockets of a velvet shooting-jacket, ornamented with large ivory buttons, such as are commonly worn by cabmen and other tap-room blackguards. His countenance was by far too dark and sinister-looking to be honest, and, as he occasionally favoured us with a few oblique and professional glances from beneath a white *castor*, half-pulled over his brow, it instinctively, as it were, reminded us of "my lord—the prisoner at the bar."

On a form against the wall, sat a tall and aged man, with a beard like a hermit, all fluttering in rags—the very emblem of wretchedness. He was relieving his uneasiness by giving his back every now and then, a comfortable rub against the wall. A little on one side of this forlorn being, at the head of the table where the landlord sat, was a character that could hardly escape the notice of the most obtuse observer, a stout active young man, in the very perfect costume of a cadger. The upper part of his person was decorated with a piece of a garment that had once been a coat, and of which there yet remained a sleeve and a half; the rest was suspended over his shoulders in shreds. A few tatters were arranged around his nether parts, but they could scarcely be said to cover his nakedness; and as for shoes, stockings, and shirt, they doubtless had been neglected, as being of no professional use. A kind of a hat (which, from a piece of the flap still remaining, showed that it had once possessed a brim) ornamented as villanous a looking head as ever sat upon a pair of shoulders—carrotty hair, that had as much pliancy as a stubble field—a low receding forehead—light grey eyes, rolling about, with as much roguery in them as if each contained a thief—a broad, snubby nose—a projecting chin, with a beard of at least a month's growth—the whole forming no bad resemblance to a rough, red, wiry-haired, vicious terrier dog, whose face had been half-bitten off by hard fighting. He was the very type of a hedge ruffian, and a most proper person to meet any one "by moonlight alone."

——"He looked as if his blood
Had crept thro' scoundrels ever since the flood."

The very sight of this model of his tribe brought vagrancy, with all her train, before our eyes, mugger's-carts, tinker's wives, bull dogs, donkeys, creels, kail pots, and all the trumpery of a gipsey's camp. This elegant individual, we found afterwards, answered to the very proper appellation of "Cadger Jack." He was leaning over the table, resting his arms on a bundle of matches, and grumbling heavily about the times, "Cadging," he said, "was gone to the the devil! He had been out ever since the morning, and had not yet broke his fast; but if he lived till Monday, he would go to the lord mayor." Here he used some emphatic language, and swore he would not stir until he got relief.

"You will get three months to the tread-mill," observed a woman, sitting opposite (the only one in the room, and a happy compound between the slut and the sot).

He d——d the tread-mill, declared he had played at up and down before now—and would go—they were compelled to give him something—the law did not suffer any man to starve, and so on.

He was rattling on in his way, without any one paying the least attention to what he said, when a lad about fourteen, decently dressed, came in, carrying a box. He placed himself beside the window, and began to display the contents of his trunk, offering for sale several respectable articles of clothing for mere trifles.

"Go home, boy," (said a man who had just come in, with his arms loaded with good things). "What brought you here? do you want to be ruined? you have run away, you young rascal, and stole them things."

The younker, who was the very image of a spoiled child and natural vagabond, replied with all the pertness and insolence of one that had been over indulged, "that the things were his—he had paid for his lodgings, and nobody had anything to do with him."

"When did he come here?" enquired the man, (the landlord by this time had gone out).

"On Thursday," he was answered.

"It is a shame," he said, "to take in so young a boy; he should have a stick laid across his back, and sent home again."

In defence of the landlord, it was argued, that if he did not take him in, others would; and that his things were safe here, which might not be the case elsewhere. This was admitted by our moralizer to be very true.

"Howsomever," observed he, "all I know is this—that if the young dog is not already a thief, I know that he has come to the right place to become one."

"Aye, that he has," drawled out a half naked lusty young fellow, raising himself slowly up from the form where he had been stretched his full length, laying upon his face, the sluggard's favourite position. Hogarth, or Joe Lisle, or any other character hunter, might have taken this youth for the very Son of Idleness. There might alternately be traced in his heavy features sluggard, loon, fool, and rascal. "Aye, that's very true," he observed, "it was coming to St. Giles's that was the ruin of me; and them there lasses," pointing to a ruddy-faced girl, who had just popped her brazen front in at the door, and who, in return for his salutation, politely placed her finger on one side of her nose, then raising the hinder part of her body touched it, in a style that would scarcely be tolerated at St. James's.

"Ah, you imp of Satan!" he bellowed out, as the young vixen scampered away between a dance and a run, and again commenced his story:

"It was coming to St. Giles's, I was saying, was the ruin of me. I robbed my father, but I got clear of that; then I robbed my mother, I got turned away for that; my sisters took me in, I robbed them, and was first to cut; at last, my aunt pitied and took care of me, I robbed her too. But I got three month for that, and—"

"Hold your tongue, you ass," exclaimed half-a-dozen voices, "the booby's mad, and should be sent to St. Luke's."

At this rebuff the hopeful youth grinned a grin something like the triumph of a fool glorying in his shame; then thrusting his hand into his bosom, was for a few moments lost in heavenly bliss, enjoying that most ecstatic of enjoyments, which King Jamie, of clawing memory, says, ought always to be reserved for kings—scratching; then rolled himself down again, to have a little more folding of the arms, and a little more slumber.

CHAPTER IV.

A BEGGAR'S REPAST.

OUR friend, who had such singular ideas in a cadging house of what ought to be, was himself but one of those who existed by his wits. Two pieces of leather hung round his feet and ankles, which for resemblance came nearer to sandals than boots. The rest of his garb, of course, corresponded.

We observed before, that, when he came in, he had his arms full of good things—among which were a sixpenny cottage-loaf, half a pound of butter, two ounces of coffee, a quarter of a pound of sugar, and half-a-dozen eggs. He now busied himself in putting those things in order, and quietly suffered the promising boy to take his will down to the road to ruin. The loaf he cut down into substantial slices, and covered them well and thickly with the rich cured cream of the cow; he put the whole of the coffee into the pan and boiled and simmered it with such attention as clearly showed that, at least in the culinary department, he was a man of taste; and although he did not mix with his beverage any of that much-talked-of continental stuff—succory, yet such was the sweet-smelling odour, as the steam wafted by us, that we could not help thinking that such highly-flavoured drink could not fail to find favour, even in the nostrils of the very Ottoman himself. This being done, he placed it upon the table, and called loudly for his mate.

And here it may be necessary to observe, that your professed vagabonds who live unmarried, always associate in pairs—like the soldier with his comrade, and the sailor with his messmate; it is probably owing to so many of the latter being members of this fraternity, that this seafaring phrase has become to be adopted. Be that as it may, however, the cadger and his mate sleep together, mess together, and share each other's good and bad luck; the most prudent of the two being always the purser.

The individual who answered to the call was a short, punchy, filthy animal, of middle age, half covered with rags. His breast was as bare and as highly coloured as the chest of a Red Indian; owing, perhaps, to sleeping in the open air, or laying among the cinder heaps of glass-houses. Jamie, for that was his name, was, however, a professed gentleman of the road; had an eye as sleepy and as cunning as a cat; and, to use his low jargon, was "up to summat," and knew "what was what."

His mate passed a few jokes upon him, at his skill in gulling swells, and taking in flats; for he was considered an adept. Jamie chucked at the compliments, and smiled at what was before them. They then fell to the viands, and ate with the hearty gusto of robust health. The eggs were certainly boiled too hard; but that defect they took good care to remedy, by softening them well with nice fresh butter, neither crying "Halt!" until there remained not the shadow of crust.

After this slight refection, like the rest of the *gemmen* who live by their means, they wiped their chins with their napkins—the cuffs of their coats—arose, and went out to that sink of ruin, the gin shop, to rinse their teeth with a little rum, that being the favourite stimulus of the begging tribe. The twopenny dram of pure Jamaica is preferred by them, and particularly those who live in the country, to any other kind of malt, or spirituous liqueurs.

CHAPTER V.

AN EVENING MEAL—A FEAST FOR AN ALDERMAN.

ALL the wandering race, such as pedlars, tramps, and hawkers of small ware, whose pursuits are in the open air, and which lead them, during the day, to an uncertain distance from their residence, never have more meals than their breakfast and their tea. But as the most of these people are no enemies to good living, they usually contrive to have their morning affair as much in the Scotch fashion as possible, and their evening refection to unite the substantiability of the English dinner, with the refreshing qualities of the tea table. Between six and seven is the hour which they in general retire from the labours of the day; and as this was the time the lodgers were now crowding in, every one carrying the eatables he intended to use, which usually consist of half a pound of bacon, quarter of a pound of butter, a pennyworth of tea or coffee, with as much sugar. These are placed upon a half-quartern loaf, and carried in one hand; and, if eggs are in season, three or four may be seen clutched in the other.

In London, and other large towns, these people, when their finances will permit, indulge in all the luxury of the cook-shop and the flesher's stall; but in country places, there is not such a variety, the bacon—a red herring, and the *et ceteras*, are mostly their choice.

Among the people who now made their appearance, were certainly some two or three labourers, but the rest were all of that stamp who scorn to live by the sweat of their brow. The frying pan was put into active motion. A couple, a man and his wife,—who by their appearance, no one would suppose that they ever partook of anything save crusts and scraps, filled the pan with nice mutton chops, by way of a relish to their bohea. Eggs and bacon, ham and eggs, ham, beef-steaks, (aye, of the prime rump, too,) mutton chops, sausages, saveloys, &c., &c., were all now with rapidity, and in their turn, soon smoking, fuming, and frying upon the fire, raising a smell almost powerful enough to satisfy the moderate cravings of a Frenchman's appetite.

The whole of the food that we could perceive that had been gathered from door to door, was one solitary plate of broken bread, which was before a broad-shouldered and able-bodied match seller; and even he, before he would allow such refuse to take its descent down his gullet, took especial care to plaster well every piece with good fresh butter—washing the whole down with an excellent cup of coffee.

It might have afforded a fine treat to the searcher after life and manners, to have observed the rough and ragged scene that was now before us. The kitchen at times was crowded to excess; and, amid the clattering of plates, fuss of cooking, and confusion of tongues, men, women, and children, feasting, drinking, singing, and card-playing, while some two or three might be seen wiling away the painful effects of an empty pocket by a soothing whiff from the favourite cutty, occasionally a half naked brute, in the shape of a man or a woman, would stagger in, their heads nodding on their shoulders, like the equally sensible and oblivious looking pate of a Chinese figure in a grocer's window; and if there was space enough, would reel a step or two, and then measure their length upon the floor, muttering sundry threatening sounds. These, of course, were soon picked up, and in their attempts to play at *a la Randall*, had their arms carefully pinioned, their bodies placed upon a seat, and laid against the wall; or, if there was room enough, were accommodated with a stretch upon the form, to snooze themselves fresh again—dreaming of the sweets of gin, and the joys of a begging life.

But perhaps a sketch or so of those strange beings, with a little of their interesting slang, will be the better way to describe such a group. By the bye, this is the place for character—the cadging house is the very spot for the pourtrayer of life, who wishes to lay claim to any thing like originality;—here Nature has her full scope, and affectation rarely shows her face.

As we were sitting, noting the various particulars that were continually passing before our eyes, and as the Poet says, catching "the manners living as they rise," a thumping step was heard coming along the passage. The door opened, and a wooden-legged weather-beaten seaman, past the meridian, with a pot of beer in one hand and a bag in the other, showed his phiz. He was dressed in the usual sailor's garb, jacket and trousers, with a black handkerchief slung round his neck, and a low-crowned glazed hat on his head. The immense breadth of his shoulders, solidity of chest, with a neck like the "lord of the pasture," gave him the weighty bearing and bold front of an eighty-four, while his open, bluff, and manly countenance at once proclaimed him to be the true man-of-war's man, and tar of old England. Jack's story is soon told:—besides being a King George's man, he had been a bold smuggler, and had his starboard leg carried away in an affray with the Custom sharks.

We were struck with something like admiration at beholding such a model of the favourite class of this country, and very naturally followed his motions, taking an interest in every little peculiarity, they being exactly what have been represented by Smollett, and other naval sketchers, as the characteristics of a tar of the old school.

Jack thumped away to a seat, clapped his pot of beer upon the table, and threw down his hat alongside. He then very gravely took out of his mouth a tolerable sized quid of tobacco, and, having safely deposited that treasure in his jacket pocket, sent, the next moment, a torrent of Virginian juice below the bars. These preliminaries being over, he proceeded to rummage forth the contents of his bag; and among the odds and ends, hauled out a substantial piece of the wing of an ox, and showed that his cruise had not been a bad one. With this goodly blunter of the keen edge of hungry appetite securely clutched in his fist, it may be supposed that the jack-knife did not lag behind; indeed, he had evidently enjoyed many a north-easter, for his appetite appeared to be of that sort which brooks no delay; never once allowing him to answer the many questions that were addressed to him, as "What cheer to-day, Jack?" &c., or so much as to give his grinders one moment's rest, save, and only then when he took a hearty pull at Messrs. Perkins and Co.

This highly-refreshing task being over, he handed a portion of his grub, and a draught of porter, to a decently-dressed young man, who had apparently nothing to chew, save his own thoughts. Then drawing from his pocket his old crony—the pipe, and stretching forth his timber toe, to feel as it were at home, commenced addressing the young fellow as follows. And here let us remind the reader, that it will be impossible for us to describe a dialogue among this class, which is of the lowest of the low, in the language of polished society; we will therefore, in lieu of the emphatic words with which they generally garnish their conversation, use the delicate but meaning dashes —— ——.

"Harry," says the tar, "have you not been at work to-day, that you look so devilish blue?" (working, by the bye, is the honest word used by those honest people for begging, they having as correct an idea of what is meant by respectable terms as their more respectable fellow men).

"Work! Aye," replied Harry, "I went out this morning with Williams. We worked all the way to Piccadilly, then down the Haymarket, along Pall Mall, and were, just beginning with some ladies in the Park, when we were stopped by a policeman, and very nigh got tapped, and —— —— if I could raise heart to cadge any more."

"Aye," cried Jack, "you were always a hen-hearted dog; but, howsomever, I had a brush to-day, myself with one of those land sharks. As I was crossing St. Martin's-lane, I saw a carriage full of ladies standing at a shop door. Up I stumped, and was just about to doff my castor (hat), when a slap on the shoulder, with 'what do you want there?' made me turn round; and there I met the ugly mug of a devil in blue. 'What's that to you?' says I. 'Oh, I thought you were going to beg.' 'Did you,' says I, 'if I had, I would have taken care not to have been such a —— fool, as to let you see me.' 'Well, well, go on, go on,' says he. I stepped on one side, and watched till my master had steered off, and then I about again, and, blow me, if one of the young ladies—and a prime un she was!—did not tip me a tanner (sixpence)."

A remarkably fine-looking man, with nicely trimmed whiskers and a long white apron, who was regaling himself with a plate of sausages to his evening souchong, here observed that there were yet some good fellows among the police. "For instance," he said, "it was only the other day, as I was working at the Middle Row, Holborn, which is my regular beat, I cadged a couple of swells. They bid me begone, or else they would call for the police. I laughed at them, and still tried it on, when one of them called to a blue devil, 'Take this fellow into custody,' says he, 'and I will appear against him to-morrow morning.' 'What's he been doing?' demanded the policeman. 'Begging,' answered the other. 'Oh, is that all?—well, if you will go on, sir, he will not trouble you.' 'Take him up directly, you scoundrel,' shouted the gentleman, 'or else, by —— I'll report you.' The policeman laughed, and walked away, leaving the swells swearing like good-uns."

The youth, whom we have before noticed as being partial to a drowsy life, now put in his word, and gave his affirmation as to the lenity of the police. His beat as he called it, was between the foot of Ludgate Hill and Blackfriars Bridge, "and neither the man who formerly looked about for the people there, nor his predecessor, ever once interrupted him in his laudable endeavours to collect pence, although he daily cadged in the very face of the guardian of the public."

It was now admitted by the whole of the company that only keep off any glaring annoyance, and the police would never say you did wrong.

"Well, well," observed Jack, "I believe, after all, London is still the place. I was once put into limbo in Norfolk, fourteen days, for simply asking a gentleman for a little money, and —— me, if the constables there won't swear that old Belzebub is white, sooner than they will let a man clear. And now," said he, shaking the ashes out of his pipe, "I must to work once more, or else there will be short allowance to-morrow, I know."

At this there was a general movement among the company; even the sluggard himself raised up his heavy lump of a body, as if necessity had just given him a call,—yawned, and fumbled with his hands about his head and breast. For, be it known, that those ease-loving people have as great a respect for the Sabbath, as Sir Andrew Agnew himself; not that they care anything for such a place as a church, but for that inherent dislike which the whole tribe have to anything in the shape of labour, and which induces them to make an extra push on a Saturday night, in order that they may enjoy the Sunday as a holiday, with the rest of the labouring classes. It must likewise not be forgotten, that the police are rather indulgent on a Saturday night, but more watchful on the Lord's day.

"Where shall we stand?" demanded a tape and thimble seller to a dealer in matches. "Tottenham Court, or Clare Market."

"Clare Market, to be sure!" answered the other; "and we will have a drop of rum at the new gin-shop. I had half a pint there this morning with Morgan, and it was prime."

"Come, Blacksmith," (the name given to the fellow whom we had designated the sloth,) said a half-naked lad, with a strong Irish accent, "Come, boy, come, we must be dodging."

"Aye," replied his heavy crony, "I suppose we must. Have you got any browns (pence) about you, Paddy?"

"Yes," said the Hibernian, "I can *sthand* a *quarthern*."

"Then, we'll go."

And accordingly they prepared, the sluggard in a soldier's flannel jacket, and a tattered pair of *breeks*, which was all that he considered requisite for the weather and his own particular profession. Paddy, a lean, pale-faced lad of eighteen, whose features bore the look of emaciation, from the continual use of tobacco—the pipe or quid never being out of his mouth, save at meals, (a short black stump now ornamented his jaws)—with a shirt upon his back that had been as much acquainted with soap as the owner's skin, and a thin pair of canvass trousers, was the finish complete to this vagabond's costume. Away they went, in the true shipwrecked sailor-begging style—their arms folded, bodies bent, and lifting their feet at every step, as if they were afraid to touch the ground for cold, and which contributed to give them that rocking gait so peculiar to the sons of the ocean—their whole frames, too, shivering as if the frosty breath of Old Winter was stealing through their veins:—the sluggard to whine and cry for melting charity at the foot of Ludgate Hill, and Paddy, in his shirt, to cadge, at ten o'clock at night, in the windiest nook on Blackfriars Bridge.

CHAPTER VI.

A QUIET SCENE.

THE kitchen was now nearly empty. A candle in a brass candlestick was placed upon each table by the under deputy, which, with the help of a good fire, made the room feel somewhat comfortable, and even cheerful. Some two or three individuals still continued to shuffle the cards; and as many women placed themselves by the fire, with their legs stretched upon the forms, to smoke and beguile away the time, until "their men," as they termed them, would come back; while perhaps two or three of the "swinish multitude" might be heard snoring away their stimulus in a corner, in sounds both loud and deep.

On a Saturday evening, from the hours of eight and nine, until eleven, every cadging house is in general particularly quiet, for the reasons we have already stated; none ever going out to work on a Sunday (the sweepers of crossings, of course, excepted), but those who are compelled from sheer necessity.

The room for some time enjoyed a tolerable degree of stillness. The master and an old female domestic occasionally entered, and made their exit. A lodger or so came home, and busied themselves in getting their refreshments. Two or three females dropped in from the women's kitchen, just by the way of having a little gossip; and, as is usual with the angelic part of the creation, scandal was the topic; how that such a one had been "carrying on," as they phrased it, all the week, getting drunk every day, and that they had never paid the landlord; and how that Mr. So-and-so was grumbling, as well he might; and how that Tom What-d'ye-call-him was going to be parted from Bet What's-her-name; "and, to tell the truth, no one pitied her; she came home *mortal* (insensibly intoxicated) twice or thrice a day, and what man *could* stand that? He had all but murdered her, the other night, but it was to no purpose; for she had taken every rag he had, even the very shirt off his back, and put them up the spout (the pawn-shop) this very morning. But as for Tom himself, he was as sober and as decent a man as ever entered a house, rarely ever seen the worse for drink above twice or thrice a week," &c., &c. With such lady-like discourse as this, then, did those patterns of excelling nature while away the time, not forgetting too, every now and then, to strengthen their language with a few powerful asseverations.

From this interesting group, we turned to observe a few individuals staggering in, when a tall countryman, with his hat slouched over his ears, and one of those velvet shooting-jackets, which we have before noticed, and which indeed is the flash coat of low life, following close after, caught our attention. The sleeves of his jerkin were slit here and there, and the white shirt (the only one we had seen that night) protruding through the rents, gave it a good deal of the appearance of the slashed doublet of former days. As he advanced into the room, we soon recognised an old acquaintance in Harry ——, of ——, in Yorkshire.

This man who now stood before us, is one of the many instances, that are to be met with in those dens, of the strange vicissitudes of life. His youth was reared in one of the first boarding schools in Yorkshire, and, for many years, he was well known at Doncaster market as a gentleman farmer; nor is it a great while ago, since this very man might be seen dashing along those streets in his one-horse chaise. But, alas! what is he now? A crawler from door to door with matches, or, when he can raise sufficient pence to purchase a stock of ballads, may be seen standing in the streets, straining himself to amuse the rabble—the inmate of a cadging house, and the companion of the lowest of the low. So much, then, for gambling and a jovial life. Notwithstanding his education, and the good society in which he must have moved, there was yet nothing of the remains of a gentleman about him; a considerable share of the fool and profligate was naturally engrafted in his character. A large black mark, in the shape of a half-moon, appeared to have been strongly indented by hard knuckles, below the left visual organ,—ornaments that are as frequently to be seen upon the inhabitants of St. Giles's, as rings are upon the visitors of St. James's. His ruffianly country dress, clownish manners, broad dialect of canny Yorkshire, with a certain cunning cast of the eye,—contracted no doubt by peering through the hedge, to see if the gamekeeper was *coming*,—all contributed to exhibit him before us, as the very *beau ideal* of a poacher.

"York! York!" was vociferated from different parts of the room, and to all of which the *bite*, or rather the bitten, answered, with good-humoured smiles. "He had just come in," he said, "to see if his mate was come hyem yet; but as he had not, he thought he could guess right weel where he wad be, and wad just step o'er to Brown's (the gin-shop) and see."

Away he went, and, in about ten minutes time, a roaring, roistering party was heard coming to the door. York entered, his arms loaded with eggs and bacon, and a glass or two the merrier. A Deaf-Burke-made fellow, an Irishman, half labourer and half beggar, who went under the name of Harlequin, reeled by his side in a state of high elevation, with two or three hangers-on, that trod close to their heels. Harlequin, filled with drink and overflowing with vanity, overwhelmed every one with noise and kindness.

The plates, &c., were soon put in order, and York showed himself no despicable cook. He made the tea, fried the eggs and bacon, and as if not to be outdone in loving kindness by his mate, now loudly proclaimed, "that if ony man was in want of *summat* to eat, to come forward; for there was plenty for all."

A man, who had been sleeping behind the table, roused himself up at the invitation, and expressed his willingness for a cup of tea.

"Nay, I'll be —— if thou shall," says York; "thou's been drunk, man, fra night till morning, and fra morning till night, these three weeks; and I say that a man that can find money to drink, can find money to eat. To get drunk," he said, turning to the company, "the matter of twice or thrice a week, is a thing that ony man is liable to, and I say that such a man is welcome to a cup of tea, and maybe *summat* to eat; but to be always drink, drinking, I say again, that a man who can find money to drink, can find money to eat, and so he shall not have a drop!"

During the latter part of this speech, the speaker's looks were directed towards the company, to see if it met with their approbation. Some two or three there were who drawled out that "it was right;" but their assent seemed to be drawn from them, more in expectation of the good things that York was about to give away, than from any real coincidence with his opinion—even such cadging house morality as this, appeared to be too rigid for their notions of right and wrong. As for the man himself, whose drowsy and dissipated looks certainly presented the very picture of a sot, quietly swallowed the affront, and laid himself down again to sleep.

The Yorkshireman, however, had apparently set his own conscience to rest, and seemed to care very little about the tranquillity of the other. He handed a piece of bacon to one, and a cup of tea to another; then thrusting a rasher into his own mouth, much in the style of a terrier griping a rat, chewed, bolted, swallowed, and gorged, until he had completely stuffed the inward man.

There was a fine contrast of national character between the Yorkshireman and his mate. The Irishman was all puff, blarney, and brag, and all the time had been in a humour either to fight or to shake hands. Nothing would serve him but to play at cards with every one of the company, offering the most tremendous odds; but, fortunately for him, there was not another purse-proud man in the room but himself. One poor fellow in particular, on whom he fastened, and who distinctly stated that he had no money, or else he would hazard a game. But this only served to set the Hibernian's froth in motion. He stormed, roused himself upon his legs, towered, and gave vent to a burst of blarney.

"Now, d—— it," says York, "I dinna like that—I dinna like it at all; attack a man that has *summat*, I say, and not one that has nought, and then that will luck *mair* like a man!" And with such hearty John Bull notions as these did *canny* Yorkshire browbeat his crony of the sister kingdom.

Some remarks were now made upon York's black eye, and various remedies proposed—such as the application of a piece of raw flesh, &c., to all of which the *Bite* did seriously incline, for, as he said, "It lucked scandalous-like to see a man with a black eye. But," says he, "Mike O'Brady maybe thinks he got clear of that; but, ye hear me say, he's mistaken? I was the other day at Epsom Races, and spent every ha'penny; and as I was coming off the course I met Tom ——, (a fellow, from whose appearance no one would suppose was worth twopence, but who, in reality, was a partner of one of those gambling-tables which are carried to fairs and races), and asked him for threepence to get a pint of *yell*. He pulled out ten shillings, and said I mot hae the loan of five pounds ony day; and when Doncaster races comes, I think I can raise other fifteen" (and to show this was no vaunt, thrust his hand into his bosom, and pulled out a handfull of the sinews of war—shillings and half-crowns), "that will be twenty, we'll make a match on it;" and raising his fist and his voice together, "we will then see which is the best man."

At this a tremendous row was heard at the door. St. Giles's was just beginning his orisons. Loud shouts, hard blows, and deep oaths were heard, with cries for the policeman, and "Murder, murder," from powerful lungs. In a twinkling the kitchen was emptied, and then came the din of strife—struggling, heavy falls, swearing, the policeman's voice, and the roar of all parties.

As soon as this animated but common affair was over, the company returned; the most of whom seemed to think it scarcely worthy of further notice; but not so with Harlequin. The Irishman was outrageous—like the war-horse, his mettle was put in motion, he whooped and bellowed, and was all kicking for a row; threw off his jacket, displaying the upper part of his body in a state of nudity, and with his clenched hand slapped his breast, which sounded like a board; then striking out, right and left, two sunburnt arms of bone, like Ossian's heroes of old, cleaving the air with their arms for the coming fight swore that he had got one black eye, and by the Holy Mother Church and Daniel O'Connell, would not lay head upon pillow this very night until he got another.

At last, after much coaxing, pulling, and hauling, he was dragged to a seat, and John Barleycorn finally overcame him, and delivered him for a time safely into the arms of Morpheus.

York sank down upon a seat, stretched his arms over the table, buried his head between them, and in an extremely short space of time, *Old Tom* gave notice that he too was fast acting as an opiate upon *canny* Yorkshire.

CHAPTER VII.

A LITTLE LITERARY CONVERSATION.

QUIETNESS was again restored. A group had gathered around the fire, to amuse themselves with a little chat. Among which was an attorney's clerk out of place, in the last stage of sottishness and vagrancy; a drunken mechanic; and a kind of decent itinerant, very pedagogue-like, an inveterate reader of the *Twopenny Police Dispatch* (the only paper the landlord took in), and a stout advocate of the Holy mother church and Daniel O'Connell, the father of the people, as he styled him. A few ungentlemanly words were exchanged between this small politician and a staunch supporter of the English Church; several topics were descanted upon, among which was the character of Wellington and his campaigns. A short but lively description was given of the Battle of Vittoria, by an old soldier in a labourer's dress.

Wellington, it was said, was not the man he was, or else the papers did not speak the truth; and, certainly, a few glaring facts were produced that they could, at least at times, make a mistake. This brought on a discussion about the management of newspapers.

One talkative fellow maintained that one newspaper was but merely a copy of another; but this assertion was clearly set aside, and the duties of an Editor and Reporter nicely discriminated, by a very equivocal sort of a *gemman*, in a great coat, whom we strongly suspected was somewhat related to the Swell Mob.

CHAPTER VIII.

THE GAMING TABLE.

THE cards had been in constant motion,—either two or three, or more, engaged with them during the whole of the evening. The card party was now augmented to about sixteen or eighteen, all players and betters, not one of whom could boast of such a thing as a shirt, save the landlord, who at this moment presided as director in chief of the ceremonies, every deference being paid to the lord of the house, as "Master this," and "Master that," and "Master the other."

Twopence to fourpence was the sum which each put down at every stake, and it was astonishing to observe how rapidly the coins were transported from one pocket to another.

"D—— it," says a match-seller, "there goes eighteenpence. I brought in two shillings; I'll now not have enough left for my Sunday's dinner."

All this was said with the most perfect good humour, and at the same time putting down the other stake.

Occasionally one of those fiend-like looks, which are said to be so conspicuous at the splendid hells, might be seen stealing even across this low swindling table. But, upon the whole, the party was very sociable, winning and losing their money with the utmost equanimity of temper.

We observed more than one put down their last penny, and then light their pipes and walk out, puffing and humming away, in search of more.

CHAPTER IX.

AN UNDER-DEPUTY.

A STRANGE phenomenon about this time grinned in at the door, his face all wrinkled with age and smiles, and an extremely short pipe in his mouth, which was no other than Ben, the under-deputy, a snub-nosed, hard-featured, squat old boy, with a horn lantern in his hand, to see if any body wanted to turn in (go to bed).

As this individual is a fine specimen of the class to which he belongs, a slight sketch, perhaps, may not be unnecessary.

The deputies, we have before stated, are the men-servants of those establishments, they being better adapted as the waiters of these noisy houses than women. Ben our present subject, had all his life been a roadsman, and lived, as the professional phrase goes, the best way he could; and now, in his old days, when his legs had become rather heavy for a tramp, had secured to himself that comfortable retreat—under-butler of the Beggar's Hall. He was well calculated to be the drudge of a common lodging house;—laborious, dull, and good-natured, answering every call, with as much patience as Francis in Henry the Fourth, with his "Anon anon!" He could sit up night and day—neither age nor toil seemed to have made much impression on his sinewy and hardened frame; indeed, to use the common saying, he was considered by all to be a durable slave.

Besides these serviceable qualities, Ben was considered a great favourite with the lodgers; was never known to utter a testy word, save and only then, when the *'bacco* grew short; like the rest of his tribe, he was an eternal smoker. This misfortune however, in being short of Virginia, was seldom of long duration. He never kept that event a secret; and, on such occasions, what could any honest-hearted cadger do, but offer their pouch to the willing old lad?

To light the lodgers to bed, was Ben's regular task—from eleven at night till three during the week, and until four on the Sunday morning.

At this summons, one or two who had become drowsy through the powerful influence of the pipe or pot, roused themselves upon their legs—stretched their arms out, and yawned, which was as much as to say, "they would follow." Ben took the hint, and moved on with his lantern, like an ostler leading horses to the stable, to show to which house in the building, and to what room, they were to repose their precious selves.

CHAPTER X.

THE RETURN;—AND A LITTLE UNKNOWN.

THE kitchen was again getting crowded. The fire once more gave notice that it was busy with chops and steaks; and as for the gambling-table, it had literally become thronged. The bawlers of catch-penny papers, or "booksellers," as they styled themselves, were now beginning to make their appearance, in parties of three or four; every one having a copy of the news he had been so loudly proclaiming stuck in the front of his hat, with that awful word, "murder," printed in large letters as the head-line; or the more melancholy announcement of the dying speech of one John So-and-so. They busied themselves in arranging their papers and dividing the gains.

We have before noticed that these people have partners or mates. A quarrel was now about to take place between a publisher and his Co. The Co. swearing that the principal was going to put him in the hole (cheat him); but after a recasting up of accounts, business was at length amicably adjusted. These lung-labourers then threw away all further care for the night, and each sought after his own individual amusement—as smoking, eating, gambling, and larking.

A singular being now entered the kitchen—one who would have afforded a fine treat to such observers as Sir Walter and the American Irving—those accurate delineators of the human race. Such places as these, we have before observed, teem with originality; they, in fact, run wild (if we may so use the expression) with character.

The man, (for the creature was in masculine garb,) was between four and five feet high; he was long armed, and one leg was rather longer than the other, which caused one of his shoulders to rise a little when he walked or stood, and which gave his shoulders, which were naturally broad, a very square appearance.

He was dressed in one of those flash coats already described whose full make, too, by no means diminished his breadth. A kind of shawl crossed his neck, or rather bosom, for his neck, was bare, in a style as if arranged by the hand of a female; and underneath of which peeped two corners of his shirt. His features were of that kind, that carried precisely the expression of those of a masculine woman; and when he spoke, it was a perfect puzzle to the stranger, to know whether he heard the voice of a man or a woman.

The creature himself (as if conscious of those singularities) affected a superior degree of manliness. Swaggered around the room, his hat half pulled over his brows, and slouched a little on one side; assuming the scowling look of a bully, and at times the flashy air of a gallant.

He had a wife; and, as if that was not enough for any man, likewise had a mistress; and, to show that he was a professed admirer of the kind of Eve, took hold of his mistress when he entered with one hand, and waving the other above his head, sung "My love is like the red, red rose," in a voice at once powerful and sweet. Then taking her upon his knee struck up "the light, the light guitar," in a style so exquisitely musical and rich, as fairly to disturb the card-table, and draw form the whole company a thundering round of applause, with "Bravo, Bill!"

He appeared to be a creature of great spirit and vivacity, dashed about, throwing himself into pugilistic attitudes, and striking out, right and left, at his cronies, in sportive play, using at the same time the true slang of low, blackguard life; as, with great emphasis, "I'll —— into you, your —— pall!" with a vast deal more of such high-toned language so appropriate for the gallant of a cadging house.[1] He fell a capering, singing all the while with great animation, and beating time most elegantly with heel and toe, and giving vent to the fulness of his spirits in shouts, as "He hows," "the Cadger Lad," "A roving life for me," &c.; and, catching hold of his wench again, thrust his hand into his bosom—pulled out a handful of silver; swore, bravadoed,—squirted tobacco juice in the grate, and boasted of always being able to earn his ten shillings a day, and thought nothing of picking up a guinea in the same time at a race or fair.[2]

This money-making man, it may be supposed, was a street singer; and was reported to be a native of that country—the land of leeks and cheese; that place where goats are said to abound—Wales.

The landlord opened the door, and gave orders for the card players to cease; it was twelve o'clock. The gamblers were loth, but the master was peremptory.

CHAPTER XI.

THE LIFE OF LOW LIFE; OR THE GLORIOUS FINISH OF THE WEEK.

"YES!" snivelled a street-preacher and psalm singer, who could scarcely hold up his head for strong drink; "we are now entering upon the Lord's day."

"Aye," observed a spouting vagabond, "it is so, old Mawworm, and you had better go to bed. You know you have your part to perform to-morrow."

"Yes!" he answered, adding a little snuff to his other stimulants, and muttered something about "God willing."

And now it was that the roar of revelry began—noise, disorder, and discord, all joined chorus. The players were let loose, and were giving vent to their different feelings, as ill or bad luck had attended them.

The lodgers were nearly all returned, every man and woman more or less in liquor. The boys of the Emerald Isle were fast approaching to that state in which they are said to be in all their glory; and nothing was now seen or heard but singing, swearing, cooking, eating, smoking, talking, larking, and quarrelling.

The first who broke the peace was a stout bare-footed fellow, a Welshman, who began beating his wife (a girl of the *pavé*), for her excessive partiality for gin.

"Are not you a pretty —— of a woman," he exclaimed, with a voice as gruff as a ruffian's could well be, "to call yourself a man's wife, to come home here, by ——, drunk, every night, while I am going about the streets all day long bawling myself hoarse!" and at the conclusion of every sentence sent her a blow of weight enough to lower one of his mountain bulls.

No one ever offered to interfere, although the woman's face was already beginning to exhibit both blood and marks; for, however that old right for a man to chastise his wife is repudiated in the other parts of society, in this refined age, yet in these walks of life, this ancient custom still holds good. Here a man is considered perfectly in the right to match his strength of arm against his wife's strength of tongue.

The fellow hammered away at his helpless helpmate with hard words and harder blows, threatening all the time a separation, and extolling to their skies the beauties and perfections of another nymph, whom he swore he would join.

Just at this moment the lady in question made her appearance; and, certainly, as far as personal looks, dress, and a more sober demeanour went, she was superior to the one in possession. The wife, who had borne beneath the weighty power of her husband, in as becoming a manner as a wife ought to do, now felt as if endowed with the nervous locks of Sampson; fired with jealousy, and backed by *Old Tom* (gin), she sprung upon her rival, and, in a moment, ribbons, caps, and hair, were twisted in the clenched hand. Down went a table and one or two forms,—men, women, and children,—and up rose yells, screams, and oaths, with all the stormy joys of fight seconding the uproar.

Old Ben rushed in, and did his utmost to restore order, but it was "no go," as they would say—family affairs must be settled. The Amazons tugged and tore at each other, if not with the fury and hate of bull-dogs, at least like their mates. The wife had secured the sweetheart by the hair, and was taking a most merciless advantage, by keeping her down upon the floor, when a Scotch sailor, wishing, we suppose, to see a stand-up affair, unloosed her hold, and let the other escape. But Sawney had, at this time at least reckoned without his host; he had been wise, he had left the devil alone; for, loosing her vengeance, she turned all her remaining rage upon the northern, and soon made something trickle down his cheeks, of more consequence than tears.

The man never retaliated, but he was not without his friend. The woman who officiated as his wife—down with the child she had in her arms— flung off her shawl, and going up to the jade who had tickled her *gude mon*, poured forth a torrent of strong round words.

"Do you think," she said, "that he has nobody to take his part, that you strike as if you were not to be struck again? No, no!" she added, "he is no man who will strike a woman except she be his own wife; but here, you — — ——, I am your," &c., &c.

"Honour among thieves!" thought we, and here's fair play among cadgers. The other, who, to use the phrase of the ring, was blood to the back bone, and in a most excellent humour to accept a challenge, was not very slow in putting herself in order for what is termed a regular.

Ben tried again for peace, but it was no use. The master was gone to the house in the Broadway, and the inmates here were wild. No nails, or tugging of hair, was brought into this action, but everything settled in the true old English style of disputing.

These paragons of the tender sex then threw themselves into attitudes that would have done honour to a Mendoza; but Sawney's wife, who was a real Lady Barrymore hussey, proved the master at arms. Tall and bony, she slashed her opponent at arm's length, with the cutting force of a Curtis and presently ended her share of the fray.

The Welshman, after having seen his battered spouse taken care of, returned and going up to the Scotchman, very gravely said,

"Joe, I believe there is something between you and me. You were always a good 'un, but I cannot allow any man to meddle with my wife."

"Say no more," said the *canny* Scot; "it's all right. No man ever heard me say, nay."

"No never!" shouted the most of the company. "You were always a trump!"

"Well then," says Taffy, "let's have this turn over, and we'll be friends yet."

And with this kind of chivalrous feeling, did these two honourable blackguards prepare to maul each other, zealously encouraged by their friends. Sawney's wife telling him, that if he did not soften that lump of goat's flesh, she would give him a lesson herself how to fist a man.

It was curious to observe how differently these people were affected, when a violent struggle was about to take place. The most of the younkers, particularly the females, got upon the window-ledge tables, and forms, but most of the veterans in vice never moved out of their seats.

The sole garments of the Scot consisted of a loose, ragged great coat, and a pair of trousers of of equal value. Wheeling himself round for the combat, in a kind of bravo style, his cumbrous coat dropped off his shoulders, with as much ease as if it had been the cloak of a Spanish duellist, and presented a frame formed for the ring. Rather under-sized, light limbed, broad chested, and strong armed, all sinew and bone, with a step as light as an Indian, and an eye as fierce as a Mohawk.

After a little play with their fists, by the way of feeling how each other stood, and an exchange or two of favours, the Scot sent in a straight right-handed hit on the throat, with as much force as if the whole weight and strength of his body had been concentrated in the blow. His man was prostrate head foremost under the bars. Taffy's lump of a body was picked up, for his soul seemed as if it had taken its flight to Davy Jones. It was all over, and Joe, the "o'er the border man," was cheered with deafening acclamations, whoops, and yells.

Harlequin, who ought to have been christened Hercules, from his Atlas-like shoulders, was now standing in the middle of the floor, like a surly boar roused from his lair, by the seat he had been sleeping upon being overturned, and, catching instinctively, as it were, that fights were going on, longed for some object on whom he could soothe his disturbed blood. He had flung his jacket over his arm, and, like a true bully, was striking his naked breast with his fist, and daring in his own low, disgusting slang, the best man in the room to turn out.

The place, at this moment, bore no bad resemblance to the infernal regions. The tables, forms, and windows were crowded, and drunkenness, ruffianism, and profligacy, were revelling in all the demoniac delights of mischief. Shouts, roars, and yells, shook the house, for the Scot to accept the challenge. Ben's voice in the din, was like a mite in the universe.

Sawney had just moved a step, to take the bear by the paw, when an apparition appeared that instantly quelled the riot.

We have heard of a story of the devil obtruding himself on a company playing at cards on a Sunday morning, and petrifying the Sabbath-breakers by the sight of his club foot; or we might imagine Jove silencing the stormy contentions of Olympus by his nod; but neither of these had a greater effect than had the blue physog. of a police sergeant showing his awe-inspiring self in at the door.

Down crouched the vagabonds; every tongue was hushed as if Silence had stilled their throats with his finger. Some took their pipes, affected to appear tranquil, but smoked very confusedly, and a slight tremor might be observed in their fingers. As for Harlequin, he stood with his naked form, and his jacket flung over his arm, with a look as condemned as if the cap was about to be placed upon him.

The policeman never once opened his lips, but moved forward, with all the commanding importance of office, as he held his lantern from one ruffian's face to another. The landlord came in, and apologized for the noise, and promised that there should be no more disturbance. The guardian of the night nodded, and walked out.

The lodgers were then entertained with a lecture, with threats of turning out, and sending to the station-house. Three or four of the most unruly were dragged away to bed and the rest left, with strong injunctions to enjoy nothing but harmless mirth.

CHAPTER XII.

ONE NOISE SUBSTITUTED FOR ANOTHER.—THE CLAMOURS OF STRIFE EXCHANGED FOR THE SONGS OF PEACE.

"Music soothes the savage breast."

IT was now two o'clock in the morning, and the streets of St. Giles's were as lively as the other back parts of the metropolis are at eleven at night. The several lodging houses round about were sending forth their various sounds, and an occasional meeting, at the doors, between two friends, with an interchange of blows, tended to keep the policeman from being weary on his duty.

Our company had been too strongly excited, notwithstanding the little check they had received, to sink into anything like sober chat. As soon as this profligate crew were left to themselves, they began to recover their spirits, by whistling and singing—beating time, with their hands upon the tables, and their heels upon the floor, so that one noise was substituted for another and the clamours of strife exchanged for the songs of peace.

The he-woman gave two or three of the sentimental songs of the day, with her usual ability; and that popular song, "The Sea," was sung in fine taste by a chorus singer of Drury Lane. *Richard's* soliloquy was ranted in stark staring style by a young vagabond who spouted from tavern to tavern for a living. An Italian air was screamed and quivered by an elderly female, who once strutted upon the stage, but who now was half bent with care, want, and blue ruin (gin). It was considered by all to be excellent, (the poor always feeling a respect for what the rich admire) although there were none there that had either hearts or heads to feel or understand it.

Some curious imitations of birds were given by a comical sort of a character, who had a good deal of wit and foolery about him. A jolly drinking song with admirable humour by a hawker of flower-pots—a stout middle-sized young fellow, in a smock frock, and a low crowned hat, with a round ruddy face, and merry eye—one, too, who was all lark, frolic and fun—a very English John with a pipe and jug.

A tall athletic youth, and a short thick-set man (brothers) dressed in flash coats, (velvet shooting jackets), ornamented with large ivory buttons, and their hats slouched on, sat in a corner smoking their pipes. They bore the exact appearance of being half poachers, and half tillers of the earth; fellows who, upon a pinch, would have no objections to take the road with a bludgeon—the very models of country blackguards. They were both in liquor—the shorter one so much so, that he had became quite obstreperous, and had once or twice interrupted the other vocalists; and now, as if unable to contain himself any longer, broke out with a strong voice slobbered a little though from too much malt—

"With a dog and gun, and all such ware,
To Donerby woods we did repair.
We went till we came to Ryburn town,
And there we drank of ale around.

"We ran these dogs till almost one,
Which made the gamekeeper load his gun—"

here the honest fellow hiccuped, which rather interrupted his harmony; at length, after a stare, as if to collect his ideas, an extra exertion, and a kind of vaunting look—again stammered forth with—

"If they had took us, and fought us like men,
We should not have valued them two to their ten."

This last burst was too much for his remaining senses; he dropped on the floor—the proper level for all topers.

But the best specimens were the street singers, that ragged, squalling class. A dirty tattered, coarse-featured wench whose visits from the cadging house could only be varied to the gin shop and pawn shop, came singing and dancing in rocking her body to and fro. She was saluted by the name, of "Bristol Bet," and "Give us the sergeant;" but Bet had tasted too much of the inspiring liquid, to answer their calls with promptitude. She footed away vigorously, to drive away care, seconding every caper with a shout, and "Jack's the lad," and slapping her body, and heel, in rather an unlady-like style.

After giving her legs a proper shaking, she laid her head a little on one side, and moving it, with her foot to keep time, screamed out, in notes both loud and shrill,

"One lovely morning as I was walking,
In the merry month of May,
Alone a smart young pair were talking,
And I overheard what they did say.
The one appeared a lovely maiden,
Seemingly in grief and pain,
The other was a gay young soldier,
A sergeant in the waggon train."

This appeared to be a real "Sweet Home" song; it went to the heart of every one in the room, who roared and bellowed applause, and thumped away with their hands and feet on the floor and tables. Bet never stopped until she had given the whole history of the Sergeant and his dearest Nancy. This poetry and music was too congenial to be easily set aside.

One of the same sex, and certainly one of the same family, a low, squat, scowling, weather-beaten looking hussey, a cadger born and bred, whose shoulders seemed as if they had been squared and rounded by a child continually laying upon them. She was the real songstress of low life; Vulgarity might have taken her by the hand. Throwing up her face which was the very symbol of bad weather and an easterly wind, doled out.

"It was down in the lowlands a poor boy did wander,
It was down in the lowlands a poor boy did roam;
By his friends he was neglected, he looked so dejected,
A poor little fisherman's boy so far away from home."

This dismal ditty, although it brought down thunders of applause, made our very flesh to creep, as it brought to our mind cauld rainy nights, starving times, Ratcliff Highway, and Whitechapel, as the other had street mobs and lads whistling and singing the popular sergeant, as they trudged home from their work at night.

They were all now in the piping mood. The wooden-legged sailor, Jack, our old friend, would have given them "Rude Boreas," but only stiff Mr. Grog would not let him; and, after one or two ineffectual attempts to clear his throat was persuaded to stagger off to his berth above stairs, respectably propped on one side by his mate, a *gemman* rather top heavy, and his noble timber supporter on the other.

York who had slept the sleep of "deep sleep," never once being disturbed by the din,—for as the seaman is used to the roar of the ocean, so the cadger is used to the roar of revelry,—now opened his eyes, and feeling his lungs and his spirits in refreshing order, made bold to rehearse the exploits of "Bauld Turpin," that mischievous blade; but, unfortunately for his talents as a vocalist, sung it so much in the dry and drawling dialect of a canny Doncaster lad, that the whole company, one and all, were fit to split their sides at York.

Songs, English, Irish, and even Welsh ditties, were bawled and drawled out, until one after one sunk into the arms of the sleeping god.

The master and his man seized this favourable opportunity to haul and coax away a number to bed. Harlequin, who had become fresh again, as he would have termed it, raised the Welshman who had had the fray in his arms, as if he had been a child, and carried him above stairs to his resting-place. York was led most lovingly out by a comely maiden from the mountains of Wales, who had lately become his wife for so long a time.

By the by, this is a great place for the ancient Britons; numbers of whom, with their Welsh names and broken English, make this house their home. There, there might be seen, William Williams fra Glamorganshire, and Hugh Morgan fra Glamorganshire, and David Jones fra Swansea, and Thomas Thomas fra Monmouthshire; with a host of round-faced, and had once been decent, man-hatted wenches.

CHAPTER XIII.

THE CLOSE OF THE NIGHT.

THE point of time was now moving fast to the stroke of four. The nymphs of the *pave*, who made this place their habitation, were all returned from the toils of the night. About a dozen or two of both sexes were gathered together around the fire, chatting of the various occurrences of the preceding day, or otherways quietly amusing themselves. The females—the most of whom cohabited with the men now in the kitchen—were a miscellaneous set; cadgers, flower-girls, servants out of place—or of that class denominated unfortunate. Some, too, went out to char and wash, and all united to their several professions the privilege of the *pave*. One or two, about a twelvemonth ago, had been the *belles* of Regent-street walk, but whose bloated cheeks and tattered shawls now made them fit denizens for St. Giles's.

A stout, middle-aged, good-looking woman, who had once been cook and housekeeper in a gentleman's family, and who still retained something of the decency and respectability of her former appearance, was now by misfortune reduced to be their associate. A few were young and handsome, and, what would appear strange in such a place, even well dressed.

There were two girls (sisters) who were romping about with a young lad, certainly in rather an unboarding-school-like manner, that particularly attracted our attention. They were both neat and clean, and genteel in their apparel. One of them, indeed, might be called beautiful. These girls had three ways of making a living. The first was that of selling flowers; the second, begging as servants out of place; the third, and certainly the best, was, to use their own phrase, "seeing gentlemen." It is a fact what we are going to state, that one of these girls has been known to make as much as five pounds a day—doubtless by the *seeing* profession and although cadgers from their birth, and born and bred, as we may say, in vice, yet it was but a few days before this, that we heard these young strumpets (for they deserve no better name) abusing an unfortunate woman who lodged in the house, using the most opprobrious language; and had at the same time, the most singular audacity to style themselves modest girls.

Of the males, the most of them were young men who had once been in better circumstances, but who now were reduced to get their living by calling papers about the streets. A few fine characters might have been picked out amongst those prodigal sons, as they stood warming their backs, or grouped together in this Vagabond's Hall.

There was an Anglo-German; he was very respectably dressed, only he had neither shoes or stockings, and though of small stature, had a voice like thunder; he was of course, considered a first-rate patterer (caller). Another, a merchant's clerk and active young man, and an excellent mimic, but a *Careless* himself. The third, a Welshman; one who might have caused a painter to halt—a model of strength; in size and form like one of his own mountain bulls, with a voice as hoarse as the winter's blast on Snowdon. He was a fine compound of ruffianism, shrewdness, and a sort of caustic humour. The fourth and last, was a tall, genteel young man, a draper, or, rather had been; he was still very smart, although much out at elbows. He had a pair of fine large, showy, sharp-pointed whiskers; was exceedingly fond of hard words, and, in his speech, superfine in the extreme. He had been highly chagrined that very night, at a person expressing surprise at seeing him at Cadger's Hall, he considering that a man might make himself respectable wherever he might be, always provided that he conducted himself with propriety; in short, maintaining to the very last, the shadow of his former consequence.

The clock chimed the warning to the final hour. A policeman came in, supporting a man he had picked up in the streets in the last stage of inebriation. Ben put out one of the lights, and gave notice that it was time to move.

The landlord busied himself in rousing two or three slumberers by sundry shakes and pushes with his foot,—not, reader to go to bed, but to go out,—they being lodgers who, having run out of coin and out of credit, were allowed for old acquaintance sake, to lie about the kitchen while it was open, but were invariably desired to depart at the lock-up hour.

The poor wretches got up, buttoned their clothes about them, thrust their hands into their bosoms, and shuffled out half asleep, a melancholy instance of the trials of the children of poverty and crime. The lodgers moved slowly off to bed, one by one; the kitchen was securely locked up, and the landlord then walked away, leaving drunkenness, misery and debauchery about the door.

FLASH DICTIONARY.

A.

ABBESS, a bawd, the mistress of a bawdyken

Abbott's Priory, the King's Bench Prison

Abram Cove, a naked or poor man, a sturdy beggar in rags

Above par, having the needful, possession of the poney, plenty of money, 'best bliss of earth'

Abram men, fellows dressing themselves in various rags, old ribbon, fox tails, begging in the streets, pretending to be mad, fellows who steal pocket books only

Abram, to sham, to slum, to pretend sickness

Academy, a brothel, bagnio

Academican, a scholar at an academy, a whore at a brothel

Academy, a floating, a hulk at Woolwich for convicts

Ack ruffians, rogues who in conjunction with watermen sometimes rob and murder on the water

Ack pirates, fresh water thieves who steal on navigable rivers

Acting the deceitful, performing, mumming, acting

Adam, a henchman, an accomplice

Adam's ale, our first father's drink, water, 'best with brandy'

Adam tiler, a receiver of stolen goods, a pickpocket, a fence

Affair of honour, killing an innocent man in a duel

All set, desperate fellows, ready for any kind of mischief

Alderman in chains, turkey and sausages

Alive, awake, fly, up, leery, acquainted with

All out, the reckoning drank out, 'How stands the account 'twixt me and vengeance?'

Ambidexter, one who snacks in gaming with both parties

Amen curler, a parish clerk

Anglers or starrers, an order of thieves who break show glasses in jeweller's windows to steal the goods

Angling cove, a receiver of stolen goods

Angelics, young unmarried ladies

Anointed, knowing, ripe for mischief

Arm props, crutches

Arch rogue, the chief of a gang of thieves, or gypsies

Arch doxey, the same among female canters or gypsies

Astronomer, a star gazer, a horse that carries his head high

As right as a trevit, the tippy all right

A pig's whisper, a grunt, 'a word 'twixt you and me'

Aunt, a bawd, sometimes called mother

Autem, a church, meeting-house

Autem cacklers, dissenters of all sects

Autem bawler, a preacher, a parson

Autem dippers, anabaptists

Autem cackel tub, a meeting house for dissenters, a pulpit

Autem divers, pickpockets who practise in churches; also churchwardens and overseers of the poor, who defraud, deceive, and impose on the parish

Autem gogglers, conjurors, fortune tellers

Autem mort, or mot, a woman of the same sect, a beggar, a prostitute

Autem quaver's tub, a quaker's meeting house

B.

BABES in the wood, rogues in the stocks or pillory

Bacon-faced, full faced

Back slums, low unfrequented parts in the metropolis

Badge coves, parish pensioners

Badge, one burnt in the hand

Badger, to confound, perplex, or tease

Badgers, forestallers and murderers

Bag the swag, pocket your portion, hide your whack

Baggage, a slut, a common prostitute

Ball o'wax, a snob or shoemaker

Ballum ranorum, a hop or a dance, where the women are all prostitutes

Balsam, rag, rhino, money

Balm, a lie

Bandog, a bum-bailiff

Bank, a depository for cash at a gaming-table

Bandy, a tanner, a sixpence

Banyan day, Saturday, when there's nothing left to eat

Bantling, a young child

Bar that, cheese it, stow it, don't mention it

Barber's clerks, conceited ignorant shop-boys

Bark, an Irishman

Barker, a salesman's servant, a prowler to pick up countrymen in the streets

Barking irons, pistols

Barnacles, spectacles

Battered bully, an old gloak, well milled huffing fellow

Bawd, a procuress, a woman that keeps a brothel

Batter, an ox

Beak, a justice of the peace, a magistrate

Beak, rum, a justice who will do any thing for money

Beak, queer, a magistrate that is particularly strict to his duty

Beaks out on the nose, magistrates out on a search night

Beaksman, traps

Bear leader, a travelling tutor

Beat, a watchman's walk

Beaver or tile, a hat

Beck or harman, a beadle

Beeswax, cheese

Belch, malt liquor

Ben or Sam, a raw, a novice

Beau traps, genteel dressed sharpers, fortune hunters

Beef, to alarm, to discover, to pursue

Belly cheat, an apron, a pad

Belly timber, food of all sorts

Belly-go-fister, a hard blow on the belly

Bene, prime, good

Bene cove, hearty fellow, a tramp

Bene bowse, good beer

Bene of gibes, counterfeiters of passes

Bene darmans, good night

Bene fakers, counterfeiters

Bender, a shilling

Benjamin, a top coat, a great coat

Betty, a small picklock

Bever, an afternoon's luncheon

Better half, an ironical name for a wife

Biddy, a fowl, a capon, or chicken; a young chicken

Bilboa, a sword, or any pointed instrument

Billing and cooing, the sexes humbugging one another; courting

Bilk, to swindle, cheat

Bing, to cut, go away

Bingo, spirituous liquors

Bingo boy, a male dram drinker

Bingo mot, a female dram drinker

Bit, money

Big'uns, men of consequence

Bit, taken in, duped

Bit, queer, counterfeit money

Bit cull, a coiner

Bit smasher, an utterer of base coin

Bit of cavalry, a knacker, a saddle horse

Bit of muslin, a flame, a sweetheart

Bitch, to, to yield, to give up an attempt thro' fear

Bitch, to, a character, or to perform any thing badly

Biting your name in, taking a large draught, drinking greedily

Blab, a prating stupid fellow, a fool

Blab, to, to nose, to chatter, to tell secrets

Black beetles, the lower order of people

Black diamonds, coals, or coal heavers

Black boy, a clergyman

Black Indies, Newcastle

Black strap, port wine

Black box or knob, a lawyer

Black spy, an informer

Black act, act of picking locks

Black cove dubber, a gaoler or turnkey

Black-legs, sharpers, fellows who lay wagers, and after losing cannot pay them; a professed gambler

Black houses, prisons

Blank, frustrated, baffled

Blarney, a wonderful story, flattery. *See* Gammon

Bleaters, lambs, sheep

Bleats, a sheep stealer

Bleak mot, a fair girl

Bleeder, a crammer, a lie

Blind, to, to cheat under a pretence

Blind harpers, itinerant vagabonds with harps

Blinker, a one-eyed horse

Block, jeminy, pipkin, head

Block houses, prisons

Blow out, a belly full, an extraordinary meal

Blow a cloud, smoking a pipe

Blow the gab, to split, to expose, inform

Blow, to split, tell, expose

Blow me tight, a sort of burlesque oath; as, If I don't I'm jigger'd, &c.

Blowings, prostitutes

Blue ruin, gin

Blue devils, blues, low spirits, horror struck

Blue pigeon filers, or flyers, thieves who steal lead from the tops of houses and churches

Blubber, to whine, to cry

Bluff, to bustle, look big

Bluffer, an impudent imposing fellow of an inn-keeper

Blunderbuss, a stupid ignorant fellow

Blunt, tip, rag, money

Boarding school, a house of correction, or prison

Bob, a shilling

Bob, a shoplifter's assistant

Bob-stick, a hog, a shilling

Bobtail, a lewd woman, or prostitute

Bobbery, a disturbance, a row

Bobbish, tol lol, pretty well in health

Body bag, a shirt

Body snatchers, bailiffs, police officers

Boggy, kiddy, covey

Bog trotters, lower orders of Irishmen

Bogey, old Nick, the devil

Bolt the moon, to cheat the landlord by taking the goods away in the night, without paying the rent

Bolt, cut, go, make yourself scarce

Bolted, hopped the twig, shuffled, gone

Bone, to steal

Bone box, the mouth

Bonesetter, a hackney coach

Bonnetter, a thump on the hat

Bon vivant, a choice spirit, a jolly dog

Booth, a place for harbouring thieves

Booked, in for it, dished

Booze, drink

Boozy, drunk

Boozing ken, a lush crib, a sluicery, alehouse

Bore, a tedious story, or a vexatious circumstance

Bordell, a bawdyken, house of ill fame

Bottle-head stupid, void of sense

Bought, anything that's dearly paid for

Bounce, to lie, to swagger

Bounceable, proud, saucy

Bower, the, Newgate

Bowsprit, cork snorter, the nose

Bow wow mutton, cag mag, dog's flesh, bad ill looking meat

Bow wow broth, broth made of stinking meat

Bow mam, a thief

Box o'dominos, mouth and teeth

Box of ivory, the teeth

Box Harry, to go without victuals

Boxed, locked up

Boxing a Charley, upsetting a watchman in his box

Brads, money

Brass, impudence

Bracket face, devilish ugly

Bravoes, bullies

Bread basket, the stomach

Breaking shins, borrowing money

Breeze, kicking up a, exciting a disturbance

Brisket beater, a Roman Catholic

Brick, a loaf

Broads, cards

Brogue, Irish accent

Broom, go, cut, be gone

Browns, copper coin

Brown Bess, a soldier's firelock

Brown suit, no go

Brown gater droppings, heavy wet, heavy brown, beer

Brush, or buy a brush, be off, make yourself scarce

Brusher, a full glass

Brushed off, run away

Bub, guzzle, drink

Bubble, to cheat, defraud

Bub, rum, good liquor

Bub, queer, bad liquor

Buff, to to swear falsely, to perjure

Buffer, a perjurer

Buffer napper, dog stealer

Bug, to damage

Buggaboes, sheriff's officers

Buggy, a one-horse chaise

Bugging, money taken by bailiffs not to arrest a person

Bull, a blunder

Bull, crown piece

Bull, half a crown piece

Bull dogs, pistols

Bulk, a fellow that attends a pickpocket, to receive stolen goods

Bully, a cowardly blustering fellow, pretended husband to a bawd or prostitute

Bully rocks, impudent villains kept to preserve order in houses of ill fame

Bully traps, pretended constables called to frighten the unwary and extort money

Bum, a bailiff

Bum'd, arrested

Bunce of dog's meat, a squalling child in arms

Bunce of fives, the closed hand, the fist

Bunch of onions, chain and seals

Bunter, a low-life woman

Buntlings, petticoats

Bung-eyed, drunk, tipsy

Burning the ken, vagabonds residing in an alehouse, and leaving it without paying the reckoning

Buss, a kiss

Bustle, ready money

Buster or burster, a loaf of bread

Button, a bad shilling

Buttering up, praising, flattering

Buttock and file, pickpocket

Buzman, a pickpocket

Buz, a pickpocket

Bye-blow, a bastard

C.

CABBAGE, tailors' perquisites

Cadger, a beggar, a scranning cove, a mean sort of a thief

Cag mag, stinking or bad meat

Cake, an easy stupid fellow

Camesa, a shirt or shift

Canary bird, the inmate of a prison

Cank, dumb, silent

Cannister, *see* Block

Cant, mock religion, language of methodists

Canter gloak, a parson, a liar

Canting, language of thieves gypsies, beggars, &c.

Canting crew, impostors who go about preaching, methodists, &c.

Canticle, a parish clerk

Cap, to, to out do, to beat

Caper merchant, a dancing master

Captain tober, first rate highwayman

Captain, head of a gang, a bully

Captain Flashman, a blustering fellow, a coward

Captain queer Nabs, a dirty fellow without shoes

Captain Sharp, a cheat, a bully

Caravan, great quantity of money

Carrion case, shirt and shift

Carrion hunters, undertakers

Castor, a tile, a hat

Cass, cheese

Cast your skin, strip naked

Cat, a drunken, fighting prostitute

Cat's meat, the constitution, the body

Cat's meat shop, an eating house

Catastrophe, behind, seat of honour

Catchpole, bailiff

Catgut scraper, a violin player

Cavil, to jaw, quarrel

Cavon, an old wig, or jasey

Chimmy, a shift

Chaff, irritating, or ironical language, to banter

Chaffer, the mouth

Chaffing crib, a drinking room where bantering is carried on

Chalk, advantage

Chalks, the legs

Chant, a flash song

Chancery, head in, said in fighting, of him whose head is held fast under the arm of his antagonist, and gets punished with little chance of extricating himself, unless he floors his man

Charley, a watchman

Charm, picklock

Chats, lice

Chates, the gallows

Chaw-bacons, countrymen, bumpkins

Cheeks, an imaginary person; nobody; as, who does that belong to? *Cheeks*.

Cheese it, stow it, give over, drop it

Cheese cutters, bandy legs

Chere amie, a bed fellow, a sweetheart

Chickster, a flame, a prostitute

Chink, rhino, rag, money

Chiv, a bleeder, a knife

Chizzle, to gammon, cheat

Chuff, jolly, merry

Chum, a bedfellow, a companion, fellow prisoner

Chummy, or clergyman, a sweep

Civil rig, a trick of the beggars to obtain by over civility

Clean shirt day, Sunday

Clankers, silver tankards

Clapper dudgeon, a beggar born

Claret, blood

Cleaned, out, mucked, having lost all your money

Clench it, complete the thing, finish the business

Clerked, cheated, imposed upon

Clicks in the gob, thumps in the mouth

Click, a knock down blow

Clinkers, fetters

Clickman toad, a watch[3]

Clink, to nab, to snatch

Clockey, a watchman

Cloy, to steal

Cly or clie, a pocket

Coach wheel, a crown piece

Cock chafer, a lady bird, a prostitute

Cloaker, drop at Newgate

Coffee-mill, watchman's rattle

Cock, a trump, good fellow

Cob, a dollar

Cobble colter, a turkey

Cog, to cheat with dice

Cogue, a glass of gin

Colt, one who lets horses to highwaymen

Coal-scuttle, a large bonnet

Cole, or coal, blunt, money

Collector, a highway robber

Colguarian, the neck

College, the King's Bench or Fleet Prison

Commission, a shirt

Commission, to shake your, to shake your whole frame

Conk, the sneezer, the nose

Convenient, a mistress

Cooler, a glass of porter

Coal-box, chorus of a song

Cod, haughty meddling fool

Come down, to give, stand treat

Come out, worse than very bad, execrable

Communicator, bell

Conk, the nose

Collar, to grab, snatch

Cooped in durance vile, to lock up in a gaol

Corinth, a brothel

Coriander seed, money

Corinthians, men of rank

Corpus, the body

Core, the heart

Coppers, halfpence

Conveyancers, thieves

Costermongers, jackass boys, venders of greens &c.

Cove, or covey, a fellow

Cove, a receiver of stolen goods

Covess of a ken, a female keeper of a brothel

Cove, lumber, a person that keeps a place for thieves

Cover me decent, a top tog, a great coat

Cover me properly, fashionable toggery

Cover me queerly, ragged raiment

Court-card, a trump

Counting-house, Mrs. Jones's, the privy

Coxy fuss, billing and cooing

Crabb shells, shoes

Crack, to break open

Cracksman, a housebreaker

Crack'd canister, a broken head

Cramp-rings, fetters

Crammer, a lie

Cramp words, sentence of death passed on a criminal

Crap, money

Crapp'd, hanged

Craping curl, an executioner

Creeme, to put money in the hands of another

Crank, gin and water

Crib, to thieve

Crib, a ken, a mean looking room

Crikey, a word of wonderment

Crimp, a decoyer, kidnapper

Crony, a companion

Cropping, the tail

Cross, on the, getting a living by dishonest means

Cross fight, a sold battle

Cross bite, to cheat a friend

Cross the herring pond, transported to Botany-bay

Crowdsman, a fiddler

Crummy, fat

Crusty, vexed, chagrined

Cub, a young child

Cucumbers, tailors

Coffin queer, a magistrate

Culch, cag-mag meat, or the refuse of anything

Culp, a kick

Cup-hot, very drunk

Cur, a sneak, a coward

Curbing law, to take goods out of window

Curl, clippings of money

Curlers, Jews who sweat gold coin by rubbing them together, for the dust

Cursitons, broken down lawyers, Newgate attorneys

Cussin, a man

Cut, sheer off, go, avoid, or shun a companion

Cut bene, to speak gently

D.

DAB, a bed

Dab, one who is clever

Dad, a father

Daffy, max, gin

Dagen, a sword

Daddle, the hand

Damn, to crush, to do away with a drama

Damp your mugs, wet your mouth, drink

Dandy, a swell, an exquisite

Dancers, stairs

Darby, ready money

Darbies, sausages, fetters

Darby's fair, the day when felons are removed to Newgate for trial

Darkey, night

Darkmans, the night

Darken the daylights, to close up the eyes

Dash, a waiter

Dash, a portion

Daylights, the eyes

Dealers in queer, passers of bad money

Dead beat, done over

Derrick to, to set out on an enterprise

Deuce, twopence

Deux wins, two pence

Dews, a crown piece

Dew-beaters, the feet

Diamond squad, folks of quality, big'uns

Diamond a horn to, to put a stone under the shoe, to sham walking lame

Diddle, spirituous liquors

Diddle cove, landlord of a gin shop, &c.

Diddle, to cheat

Die proud, or game, to die with courage, or hardened

Dimmock, money

Dimber, handsome pretty

Dimber damber, the king of the canting crew

Dimber cove, a pretty cove, or fellow

Dimber mot, an enchanting girl

Ding, to throw away

Ding boy, a rogue, knave, or sly fellow

Dinger, a pickpocket, or thief

Dipper, anabaptists

Dock yarder, a skulk in any sly place

Doctors, false dice

Doff, to uncover, take your hat off

Dollop, a handful

Dominic, a parson

Done brown, done over, queered, floored

Donovans, potatoes

Donkey's ears, a false collar

Don't name em's, inexpressibles, breeches

Dorse, a place of rest

Douse the glimm, blow out the light

Doughey, a baker

Down, fly, awake, knowing

Down in the mouth, having nothing to say, low spirited

Doxy, girl of the town

Dozing crib, a sleeping room

Drag, a cart or waggon

Drap, a drop

Draw it mild, gently

Draw latches, robbers of houses

Drawers, stockings

Drawing a cork, giving a bloody nose

Drawing a thimble, picking a pocket of a watch

Drawing a wiper, picking a pocket of a handkerchief

Drawing a long bow, telling a lying story for truth

Dromedary, a clumsy thief, a young beginner

Drop, the squeezer at Newgate

Drops, who go about to public houses to cheat unwary countrymen at cards

Droppings, heavy wet, beer

Dub, a key

Dub the jigger, fasten the door

Dubber, a picker of locks

Duds, togs, clothes

Duds cheer, ragged, poor

Duffers, swindlers, who go about with articles pretending they are smuggled and to sell them at an apparently cheap rate

Dummy, a stupid fellow, one who has nothing to say for himself

Duke of limbs, a deformed person

Dunnaken, if it be necessary to explain the word, a privy

Dupe, a victim to artifice and misrepresentation

Durance vile, prison

Dutch reckoning, bad reckoning

Dust, money

Dustman, sleep, or drowsiness

E.

EARWIG, a crony, a close friend

Earth stoppers, horses feet

Elbow shaker, a dice rattler, a gambler

English Burgundy, strong beer

Eriffs, young thieves in training

Eve droppers, vagabonds who rob hen roosts

F.

FACER, a blow on the face, a bumper

Fadge, a farthing

Fag, to ill use, to work hard

Fakements, scraps, morsels

Fast trotters, good horses, rum prads

Fam, a ring

Fams, or fambles, hands

Fancy, the ton of low life

Farmer, an alderman

Fastener, a warrant

Faulkner, a juggler, a tumbler

Fawney, a ring

Feck, to, to discover which is the safest way of obtaining stolen goods

Feeder, a spoon

Feint, pawnbroker

Felt, a hat

Fem, a hole

Fence, a receiver of stolen goods

Fencing ken, a house where stolen goods are deposited

Feret, a pawnbroker

Fib, to fight, to box

Fibbing, pummelling a head while in chancery

Flich me some panea and causau, cut me some bread and cheese

Fiddler, a sixpence

Fiddle, a watchman's rattle

Fiery snorter, a red nose

Field lane duck, a baked sheep's head

Fig out, to dress

Figure, a little boy put in at a window to hand goods to his accomplices

Filcher, a thief

File, a rum, an odd fellow

Filch, to steal

Fin, arm

Fishfag, a woman that sells fish

Fishooks, the fingers

Fives, the fingers

Fives, a bunch of the fist, the hand closed

Flag, groat, fourpence

Flame, a bit of muslin, a sweetheart

Flankey, the behind, the part you sit on

Flash of lightning, a glass of gin

Flash, language used by thieves, gypsies; to sport

Flashman, a prostitute's bully

Flash cove, the keeper of a place for the reception of stolen goods

Flashing his gab, showing off his talk

Flash his ivory, showing off his teeth

Flat, a raw, an inexperienced fellow, a fool

Flat-catcher, an article to dupe the public

Fleec'd, clean'd out, stript

Flick, to cut

Flicker, a drinking glass

Flimsies, Bank of England notes

Flipper, the hand

Floating academy, the hulks at Woolwich for convicts

Flogger, a whip

Floored, knocked down

Floorers, fellows who throw people down in the street, &c. when their companions under the pretence of assisting, rob them

Flowers of society, the ornaments of high life, big'uns

Fly, up, acquainted with

Flyers, shoes

Flying colours, to come off with, to come off with luck, to do anything with advantage to yourself

Flue faker, a chummy, a sweep

Fogle, pocket handkerchief

Fogo, stink

Fog, smoke

Fogus, tobacco

Fogay, a stupid fellow

Footing, money paid by a prostitute when going among her companions, also money paid on entering into any trade or calling amongst mechanics

Fork, a pocket

Fork it out, to produce anything by the hand

Forks, fore and middle fingers

Fresh water bay, Fleet-market

Frisk, mischief

Frontispiece, the face

Frow, a prostitute

Frummag'd, choked, or hang'd

Frumper, sturdy blade

Fudge, gammon

Fuller's earth, gin

Fumbles, gloves

Funk, stew, to fret

Funk, to cheat, alarm, to smoke, stink

Funkers, the very lowest order of thieves

G.

GAB, the mouth

Gaff, a fair

Gaffing, tossing with the pie man

Gag high, on the whisper, nosing, telling secrets

Gag low, the last degree of beggary; to ask alms in the streets with a pretended broken limb

Gage, a quart pot

Gaggler's coach, a hurdle

Galters, blacklegs; gamblers

Galligaskins, breeches

Gams, the legs

Game, courageous, sturdy, hearty, hardened

Gammon, falsehood or bombast

Gammoners, cheats, swindlers

Gan, the mouth

Gape seed, anything that attracts the sight

Garnish, money demanded of people entering into prison

Gay tyke boys, dog fanciers

Gee, suitable; that won't gee, won't do

Gelter, money

Gentry cove, a gentleman

Gentry ken, a gentleman's house

George, yellow, a guinea

George, a half crown piece

Gig, fun, nonsense, ready, on the alert

Gill, a cove, fellow

Gills, cheeks

Gin spinner, proprietor of a gin shop

Grinny, an instrument to lift up a grate, in order to steal what articles are in the window

Giving turnips, to cut acquaintance, to shun any body

Glazier, one that breaks windows and show glasses in order to steal goods exposed for sale

Glibe, a writing

Glim, the candle, or light

Glims, peepers, eyes

Glims flashy, a person in a passion

Glim Jack, a link

Glimstick, a candlestick

Glim fenders, hand irons

Gloak, a man

Glue, the lady's fever, venereal disease

Gnostics, knowing ones

Go it, keep on

Go slow, draw it mild, easy

Go by, to rise by superior force, turn the tables, against you

Gob stick, a silver table spoon

God permit, a stage coach

Goggles, the eyes

Goldfinch, yellow boy, gold coin

Gone to pot, become poor in circumstances, gone to the dogs

Goose, to, to hiss like a goose

Goth, A, a fool, an idiot

Grabb, snatch

Grab the bit, to seize the money

Grabbed, taken, or apprehended

Grand strut, Rotten Row, Bond Street

Grand twig, in prime style

Grannum gold, old hoarded coin

Gravel digger, a sharp toed dancer

Gravel tax, money robbed from people on the highway

Grease, money

Greek, St. Giles's, slang language

Greeks, gamblers, blacklegs

Green bag, lawyer

Green, raw, unlearned

Greenhorn, a sponge, a raw countryman

Grig, merry fellow, merry companion

Grinders, the teeth

Groaners, a sort of wretches who attend meetings, sighing and looking demure; in the meantime their pals pick the pockets of those persons who may be in the same pew with them. They also rob the congregation of their watches, as they are coming out of church; exchange their hats for good ones jocosely called *hat making*; steal prayer-books, &c.; also fellows who go around with street preachers, who, while the mock parson is preaching, they pick the pockets of the listeners

Groat, a flag, fourpence

Grogham, a horse

Gropers, blind men

Gropusses, the pockets

Ground sweat, to be buried

Grub, provender, victuals

Grub and bub, victuals and drink

Grunter, a pig

Grunter, a bob, shilling

Guinea pig, a fellow who receives a guinea for puffing off an unsound horse

Gull, to cheat, circumvent

Gulpin, a raw, a yokel unlearned

Gum, abusive language

Gun powder, an old woman

Gutter lane, the throat

Gutting a quart pot, drinking a pot of beer

H.

HACK, a hackney coach

Half and half, half seas over, tipsy

Half a bull, half a crown

Half a hog, half a shilling

Half a grunter, sixpence

Half nap, venture, hesitation

Hams, breeches

Hammering, excessive heavy thumps with the fists

Hamlet, high constable

Hand over, to bribe evidence not to appear against a culprit, to drop an argument, an action

Handle the ribbing, to knock the ribs about

Hang it up, to leave a reckoning unpaid at a public house

Handle, a tool, a silly fellow

Hard up, in a queer way, money all gone

Harman, a constable

Harmans, the stocks

Havannah, under a canopy of, sitting where there are many persons smoking tobacco

Hawks, swindlers, sharpers

Hawks, an advantage

Hear anything knock, do you take the hint

Hearing cheats, ears

Heave, to rob

Heavy brown, beer

Heavy plodders, stock brokers

Hedge taverns, public houses on the road side, little frequented by travellers

Heavers, breasts

Hedge creeper, the meanest order of thieves

Hedge bird, mean scoundrel

Hedge, to secure a bet by betting on the contrary side

Hedge off, slink off to avoid serious consequences

Hell, a gambling house

Hell cat, a lewd abandoned woman

Hell hound, profligate impudent fellow

Hempen casement, a halter

Hempen furniture, money rewards for convicting felons by thief takers and others; commonly called blood money

Hempen widow, a woman whose husband has been hang'd

Hen, woman

Hick Jop, a bumpkin, a fool

Hick Sam, a country fellow, a fool

High pads, thieves, or footpads who rob on the highway, on foot, of the same class as scamps and spicers

High flyer, an audacious impudent woman

High tide, having plenty of money

High tobers, the highest order of thieves, who rob on the highway, well dressed and mounted on fine horses

High gloak, well dressed highwayman

High jinks, gamblers, a set of fellows who keep little goes, take in insurances; also attendants at the E.O. tables and at the races; fellows always on the look out to rob unwary countrymen at cards

Hob, a bumpkin, a clodhopper

Hobbled on the leg, a transported felon ironed on the leg, and sent on board the hulks

Hog, a shilling

Hog grabber, a sneaking mean fellow, a cadger

Hog grunter, a close fisted narrow-souled, mean fellow

Hoisters, shop-lifters, fellows who go into shops, and under the pretence of buying goods, generally conceal some article under the sleeves of the coat, mostly frequenting jeweller's shops

Hoister mots, women who go into shops and steal some small article

Holy land, St. Giles's, from St. Giles's being the patron saint of *beggars*

Hoofs, the feet

Hoof it, to walk

Hooked, overreached

Hookers, thieves

Hop, a sixpenny, a dancing room, where sixpence is the price of admission

Hop merchant, a dancing master

Hop the twig, run away

Harness, watchmen, constables, police officers

Hot flannel, liquor made of beer and gin, with eggs, sugar, and nutmeg

Hue, to whip, lash

Huff, a bullying, cowardly, fellow

Huggar, drunk

Hum box, pulpit

Hum, a liar, a canting deceitful Wesleyan methodist

Hum, to humbug, deceive

Hums, people at church

Humpty dumpty, boiled ale and brandy

Hunting, drawing unwary people to play

Hush still, quiet

Hush money, money given to compound felony

Huskey lour, a guinea, gold coin

I.

INDEX, the face

Ignoramus, a stupid fellow, a novice

Inexpressibles, breeches

Ingle boxes, jacks tipped with silver and hung with bells

Ingler, horse dealer of bad character

Interlopers, lazy fellows who are dependent on the generosity of their friends for support

Irish apricots, potatoes

Irish evidence, false witness

Irish legs, thick legs

Iron doublet, a parson

Iron, money

Itch land, Scotland

Ivories, the teeth

J.

JACK, a farthing

Jack Adams, a muff, stupid fellow

Jack at a pinch, a hackney parson

Jack in the box, a sharper, a cheat

Jack cove, a sloven, dirty fellow

Jack-a-dandy, a little impertinent fellow

Jack pudding, merry Andrew, a clown

Jacken closer, a seal

Jacob, a ladder,

Jacobites, sham or collar shirts

Jackrum, a license for marriage

Jam, gold ring

Jarvey, hackney coachman

Jasey, a wig

Jaw, abusive language

Jehu, a coachman

Jemmy, twopenny, head

Jenny, a picklock

Jet, a lawyer

Jet Autem, a parson

Jew, an over-reaching fellow

Jig, a trick

Jigger, a door, bolt, or private still

Job, guinea

Jobber knot, a tall stupid fellow

Jock gagger, fellows who live on the prostitution of their wives, &c.

Joe, an imaginary person, nobody; as, Who do those things belong to? Joe

Jolter head, a heavy dull blustering landlord

Jones's, Mrs., the coffee house, privy

K.

KATE, a picklock

Keep up the ball, to live and be jolly

Keep the line, to, to behave with decorum

Ken, a cribb, room

Ken-cracker, house breaker

Ken Bowman, a well furnished house

Ken, flash, a house where thieves and vagrants resort

Ken miller, house breaker

Kick, sixpence

Kick, to borrow money, to ask a favour

Kick the bucket, to expire

Kicksies, breeches

Kid, a fellow thief

Kiddies, flash fellows

Kid lays, villains who defraud boys of their parcels and goods

Kiddiess, a slap up well-dressed girl

Kid, with, pregnant

Kid-nappers, fellows who steal children, and decoy countrymen and strangers in the street, to rob them; also recruiting crimps

Kidwy, a thief's child

Kill devil, new rum, from its pernicious quality

Kinchin, a young child

Kimbau, to defraud, cheat

King's mots, female children carried on the backs of strollers and beggars to excite the pity of the public

King's picture, king's head on gold coin

Kinchin coves, fellows who steal children for gypsies, beggars, &c.

Knacker, an old good for nothing horse

Knife it, stow it, be quiet

Knight, a poor silly fellow

Knight of the awl, a snob, cobbler

Knight of the hod, a brick-layer's labourer

Knight of the road, a highwayman

Knight of the brush and moon, a drunken fellow

Knight of the post, a perjurer, false swearers, fellows employed to give false evidence

Knight of the blade, a bullying sham captain, a braggadocio

Knights of the rainbow, waiters, footmen, lacqueys

Knowledge box, the jemmy, head

Knuckles, pickpockets

Knuckle dabs, ruffles

Ky-bosh on, to put the, to turn the tables on any person, to put out of countenance

L.

LADY-BIRD, a sweetheart, bedfellow

Laced woman, a virtuous female

Lady's man, an obsequious fellow to females

Lady in mourning, hottentot girl

Lag, to transport

Lagged, transported

Lagger, a person working on the water

Lame ducks, defaulters at the Stock Exchange

Lambskin men, the judges

Lantern, dark, a servant or agent that receives a bribe to conceal a robbery

Lap, butter-milk, whey

Lap, rum, good liquor

Lap feeder, a spoon

Lapping your congou, drinking your tea

Lark, a bit of mischief, fun

Leading strings, the control of friends

Leery, fly, up, acquainted

Leerers, the eyes

Left, over the, no go, it won't do

Leg bail, running away

Leg o'mutton sleeves, large sleeves worn by the ladies

Levanters, persons who run away from their debts of honour

Lib, to live together

Lib ken, lodging house

Libbege, a bed

Lifter, a robber of shops

Lighting a candle, sneaking out of a public house with out paying the reckoning

Light blue, gin

Lightning, gin

Lightning, a noggen of, a quartern of gin

Lightments, the day

Lil, a pocket book

Lily white, a snowball, a black, a chimney sweep

Limbo, prison

Line, getting into a, confusing a person, imposing on any body's belief by joking

Lingo, slang, language

Link it, turn it out

Lipish, saucy

List, or Loist, shop-lifting, robbing a shop

Little Barbary, Wapping

Little shillings, love money

Lively kid, a funny fellow, a brave man

Loap'd, run away

Lob, money till

Lob, an easy foolish fellow

Lob lolly, a queer cooked mess

Lob's pound, a prison

Lobsters, soldiers

Lock, a warehouse for the reception of stolen goods

Lock, rum, being in good health; rich, clever, expert

Locksmith's daughter, key

Loge, a watch

Loose house, round house or cage

Lord, a deformed hump-backed person

Lour, money

Low-water mark, having little money

Lugs, or listeners, the ears

Lully, wet linen

Lullaby cheat, an infant

Lully priggers, the lowest order of thieves, who decoy children to some bye place and rob them of their clothes

Lully snow prigging, stealing wet linen from hedges

Lumber ken, a pawnbroker's shop

Lumber the ticker, to pawn a watch

Lurch, in the, to be left behind, to sneak, to hang on

Lush cribs, sluicery's, gin shops

Lush, drink

Lush ken, an alehouse

Lushingtons, drunkards

M.

MACE, to rob, steal

Mackry, the country

Mad Toms of Bedlam, fellows who counterfeit madness in the streets, and after beating themselves about, spit out some blood, in order to convince the too feeling multitude that they have injured themselves by violent struggles, and so obtain relief: they have a small bladder of sheep's blood in their mouth and when they choose can discharge it

Made, stolen

Mag, halfpenny

Make, to, steal

Malty coves, beer drinkers

Mary-le-bone kick, a kick in the belly

Marrowbones, the knees

Mat macers, fellows and old women who go round in a morning when the servants are cleaning the doorways and steal the mats, &c.

Maunder, beggar

Maundering, begging

Mauns, tip us your, give me your hand

Mawley, the fist

Mawmouth, one that splutters in his talk

Max, gin

Mazzard, the head

Mest, to spend

Middle-piece, the stomach

Mill, thump, fight

Mill the glaze, breaking windows or lamps

Mill the ken, break open the house

Mill his nob, break his head

Mill clapper, a woman's tongue

Milldoll, to beat hemp in Bridewell

Miller, a boxer

Missing, courting; to be gone or away

Misstopper, a coat and petticoat

Mizzle, go, begone

Moabites, bailiffs and their crew

Mog, a lie

Moisten your chaffer, drink

Monish, tip us the, give me the money

Monkey up, being in a violent passion

Mopus, a halfpenny

Moon cursers, link boys

Moonshine, nonsense, flummery

Morriss off, to run away

Mother, a name for the keeper of a brothel

Mother's milk, rum, boose, good liquor

Mots, cyprians, whores

Mount, to give false evidence

Mounter, a common perjurer, villains who give false evidence and become bail for fellows of their own stamp

Mouth, a stupid fellow, a novice

Move, an incident, an action in life

Mower, a cow

Muck, money

Muck, to, to clean out, to win all a person's money

Muck'd, lost all at play, no money left

Mud pipes, thick boots

Muff, a raw, a silly fellow

Mufflers, sparring gloves

Mug, the face

Mugs, cutting of, making faces

Mullygrubs, the belly ache

Mummer, the mouth

Mummers, strolling players, mountebank speakers, gypsies, and beggars who tell pitiful stories to excite compassion

Muns, mouth

Mumbling cove, a sturdy ill-natured landlord, shabby fellow

Murphies, potatoes

Muzzle, the mouth

N.

NAB, to steal

Nabb'd, taken

Nail, to lay hold

Natty lads, young thieves

Nash, to bolt, to run away

Needful, money

Never wag, man of war, the Fleet Prison

Neat thing, good liquor

Nab, a hat

Nabs, a person to either sex; a familiar way of talking; as, How are you my Nabs

Nob the bib, to cry and wipe the eyes

Nab the rust, to receive the money

Nab the noge, to receive a guinea

Nab the clout, steal a handkerchief

Nab the cramp, having sentence of death passed

Nab the bung, to receive a purse

Nask, a prison

Napper, or Nads, a sheepstealer

Napper, the head

Ne'er a face but his own, not a farthing in his pocket

Newlicks, or Noolucks, a person not known, an imaginary being, said to be a kin to Joe, Cheeks, &c.

Nibble, thieve, steal

Nicks, nothing

Nim, to steal

Nimmer, a thief of the lowest order

Niggers, fellows who clip and file gold coin

Nig, clipping of money

Nick it, to win a wager

Nip, a cheat

Nipperkin, half pint measure

Nix, or nix my doll, nothing

No go, it won't do, a bad experiment

Nob, the head

Nob, the head; a fellow carrying a high head, a man of money, of respectability

Nob thatcher, a hat maker

Nob, old, a favourite game used by sharpers, called pricking in the hat

Nobblers, blows, thumps

Noddle, empty headed, shallow pated, stupid

Noll, a wig

Noodle, a sawney

Norway neckcloth, the pillory

Norfolk capon, a soldier, a red herring

Nose, a, one who splits or tells

Nose, to, to expose, tell

Nozzle, the nose

Nub, the neck

Nubbing, hanging

Nubbing cove, the hangman

Nubbing ken, the sessions house

Nubbing cheat, the gallows

Nail gropers, people who sweep the streets in search of old iron, nails, &c.

Nunnery, a brothel

Nurse, to cheat

Nutty, fond

Nut crackers, the pillory

Nutmeg grater, the beard

O.

OAK, a rich man of credit, substance

Office, warning, notice

Ogles, the eyes

Ogles in mourning, black eyes

Ogles, rum, fine piercing eyes

Oil of palm, money

Old One, or Old Harry, names for the devil

Old Tom, good gin

Old toast, a brisk lively old man

Oliver, the moon

Oliver widdles, the moon shines

Oliver sneaks, the moon hid under a cloud, has got his upper Ben on

Oli compoli, a rogue of the canting crew

On the pot, being in trouble, vex'd

On the mallet, having goods on trust

One two, two blows succeeding each other

One in ten, a parson

Optics, the eyes

Operators, pickpockets

Os chives, bone handle knives

Out and outer, a rum'un, a good fellow at any thing, a trump

Ousted, turned out, thrown

Over the left, it won't do, no go

Over the bender, over the bridge

Overseer, a fellow in the pillory

Owlers, runners and smugglers of wool

P.

PAD, a highwayman who robs on foot

Pad it, to walk

Palm, to fee, to hand over

Pallaird, beggars who borrow children, the better to obtain charity

Panum, victuals

Panum struck, very hungry, wanting something to eat

Pantler, a butler

Param, bread

Parings, clippings of money

Panter, heat

Pat, an accomplice or companion

Patter, slang

Patter slang, to talk flash

Pattered, tried in a court of justice for felony

Pave, the pathway

Pavier's workshop, the street

Peck and boose, victuals and drink

Peel, to strip

Peeper, looking glass

Peepers, eyes

Peel your skin, strip, pull off your clothes

Peery, suspicious

Peg a hack, to drive a hackney coach

Peg, or peg stick, a bender, shilling

Peg tantrums, dead

Penance board, pillory

Persuaders, cudgels or spurs

Peter, a trunk

Peteresses, persons who make it their business to steal boxes from the backs of coaches, chaises, and other carriages

Pewter, money

Pewter, to unload, to drink porter out of a quart pot

Philistines, bailiffs and their crew

Phizog, the face

Pickling tubs, Wellington, or top boots

Picture frame, the gallows, or pillory

Pig, a sixpence

Pigman, a trap, or bailiff

Pigeon, a meek stupid easy fellow

Pike off, run away

Pinch, to steal money under pretence of getting change, *see* Ringing the changes

Pimple, the head

Pinks of fashion, dashing fellows

Pins, the gams, legs

Pippin, funny fellow, friendly way of expressing one's self as 'How are you, my Pippin?'

Planket, concealed

Pockets, to let, empty pockets, no money

Point non plus, neither money nor credit

Poke fun, to chaff, joke

Poke, a bag, or sack

Poker, a sword

Poney, money, £50

Pop, to pledge or pawn

Poplers, mess of pottage

Poppers, pistols

Potato, drop it like a, to drop any thing suddenly

Potato trap, the mouth

Potato, red hot, take a, a word by way of silencing a person, a word of contempt

Pot scum, bad or stinking dripping

Pothooks and hangers, short hand characters

P's & Q's mind your, mind what you're at

Poundage cove, a fellow who receives poundage for procuring customers for damaged goods

Prad, a horse

Prancers, horses

Prate, roast, a loquacious fellow

Pratt, buttocks

Pricking in the wicker for a dolphin, stealing bread from a baker's basket

Prigs, thieves, pickpockets

Prime twig, high condition

Prog, victuals

Prog, rum, good victuals

Prog, queer, bad victuals

Property, an easy fellow, a tool made use of to serve any purpose, a cat's paw

Provender, a person from whom any money is taken on the high road

Pudding house, the workhouse

Pull, having the advantage over an adversary

Pull out, come it strong

Punch, a blow

Punish, to beat in fighting

Punisher, one who beats soundly

Pupil's straits, school tuition

Purgatory, trouble, perplexity

Purl, royal, ale and gin made warm

Purse, a sack

Put, a country fellow, silly, foolish

Putty and soap, bread & cheese

Q.

QUARROMS, a body

Queer, base, doubtful, good for nothing, bad

Queer bit makers, coiners

Queer buffer, sharp inn keeper

Queer street, to be in, in a quandary

Queer cove, a rogue, villain

Queer ogles, squinting eyes

Queer patter, foreign talk

Queer rotar, a bad ill looking coach

Queer rag, ill-looking money, base coin

Queer blowing, ugly wench

Queer gill, suspicious fellow

Queer plungers, fellows who pretended to be drowned

Queer cole makers, coiners of bad money

Queer lap, bad liquor

Queer beak, strict justice, upright judge

Queer rag, bad farthing

Queer bit, counterfeit money

Queer lully, deformed child

Queer tats, false dice

Queer vinegar, worn out woman's cloak

Queer belch, sour beer

Queer cove, a turnkey

Queer bid, insolvent sharpers who make a practice of billing persons arrested

Queer cat lap, bad tea

Queer chum, a suspicious companion

Queer pops, bad pistols

Queer put, an ill-looking foolish fellow

Queer thimble, good for nothing watch

Queer hen, a bad woman

Quota, whack, share

Quod cull, a gaol keeper

Quail pipe, woman's tongue

Queer prad, broken knee'd horse

Queer lambs, bad dice

Queer Nantz, bad brandy

Queer nicks, breeches worn out

Queer dogen, rusty sword

Queer buffer, a cur

Queer harmen beak, a strict beadle

Queer gum, outlandish talk

Queer glim, a bad light

Queer ken, a gentleman's house without the furniture

Queer doxy, a clumsy woman

Queer booze, bad beer

Queer amen curler, a drunken parish clerk

Qui tam, a shark, lawyer

Qui vive, on the alert, in expectation

Quid, a goldfinch, sovereign

Quiz, a queer one, a gig, an aboriginal

Quod, prison

R.

RADICAL, Hunt's breakfast powder, roasted corn

Rag, money; I've no rag, meaning I've no notes

Rag, blow up, rap out, scold

Rainbow, a tailor's pattern book

Rainbows, gay young bucks

Rain napper, an umbrella

Rap, I'm not worth a rap, I've got no money

Rap, give evidence, take false oath

Rap out, to swear, blow up, be in a passion

Rat, drunken man or woman taken in custody for breaking the lamps

Rattling cove, a hackney coach man

Rattling gloak, a simple easy fellow

Rattling mumpers, beggars who ply coaches

Ready, money

Reader, a pocket-book

Red rag, the tongue

Red rag, give your, a holiday, hold your tongue

Red tape, Cognac, brandy

Regular, in proper course

Regulars, persons thus called from their leaving parties of pleasure at eleven or twelve o'clock at night, to the no small discomforture of many an out-and-outer

Regent, half a sovereign

Resurrection men, fellows who steal dead bodies from the church yard for the surgeons

Rhino, grease, money

Ribbon, money

Ridge, gold outside of a watch or other article

Ridge cove, a wealthy goldsmith

Riff raff, black beetles, the lower order of people

Rig, fun, game, diversion

Rig out, a suit of clothes

Rig conoblin, cutting the string of large coals hanging at the door of coal sheds

Rigging, clothing

Right and fly, complete

Ring, to exchange one article for another

Rise, a, a disturbance

Rivertick, tradesman's books

Rivits, money

Roger, a portmanteau

Rooled up, put in a spunging house

Romoners, fellows pretending to be acquainted with the occult sciences, fortune tellers

Rome ville, London

Rookery, an ill furnished house

Roses, nobility

Rotan, a coach

Rum glimmer, head of the link boy

Rum bodick, dirty shabby fellow

Rum beak, sensible justice

Rum doxy, fine made wench

Rum drawers, silk stockings

Rum gloak, well dressed man

Rum Nantz, good brandy

Rum ghelt, or rum cole, new money

Rum squeeze, wine or other liquor given to fiddlers

Rum prancer, fine horse

Rum rufe peck, Westphalia ham

Rum prad, a highwayman's horse

Rum duke, queer old fellow, rich man

Rum gill, a man who appears to have plenty of money

Rum rush, a number of villains rushing into a house in order to rob it

Rum gutters, cape wine

Rum quid, good guinea

Rum chaunt, good song

Rum booze, good wine, or any liquor

Rum buffer, valuable dog

Rum cly, a full pocket

Rum feeder, large silver table spoon

Rum gaggers, cheats who tell wonderful stories of their sufferings at sea, in order to obtain money

Rot gut, swankey, small beer

Row, disturbance, 'and in the ken to breed a row'

Roysters, noisy, turbulent fellows, rude vile singers

Roundyken, the watchhouse

Rumpus, a scuffle

Rub, an obstacle in the way, to run away, to make off

Rub out, when its dry, all right when its forgotten

Ruffman, any person who handles a thief roughly; the wood, hedges

Rugg, all right and safe

Rug carrier, an ensign

Rum blowing, a handsome girl

Rum hopper, a waiter at a tavern

Rum mot, a woman of the town

Rum bob, a shop till

Rum peepers, fine looking glasses, or bright eyes

Rum speaker, good booty

Rum job or rum dagen, a handsome sword

Rum quids, guineas

Rum, pad, the high road

Rum maundy, fellows who counterfeit the fool, going about the streets in order to obtain charity

Rum kicks, breeches

Rum file, or rum diver, a female pickpocket

Rum dropper, a vintner

Rum cove, good natured landlord

Rum fun, sharp trick

Rum bung, full purse

Rum bow, rope stolen from any of the king's dock-yards

Rum clout, handkerchief

Rum bluffer, a jolly host

Rum bleating cheat, a fat sheep

Rum back, good natured Irishman

Rum barking irons, prime pistols

Rum dumber, good natured prince of the canting crew

Rum quod cull, a gaoler

Rum, or monogin, good, the most valuable of any thing jewels, diamonds

Rum'un, a trump, a good fellow

Rum ti tam with the chill off, good, slab up, the tippy, excellent

Ryder, a cloak

S.

SACK, a pocket

Sack, to, to take up

Sam, a foolish fellow, an idiot

Sam, to stand, to pay for all

Sangaree, rack punch

Sans prisado, a person who comes into company without any money

Saving one's bacon, to escape with a whole skin, to evade any accident

Seedy, poor, miserable looking without money

Scamp, a thief

Setter, persons using the haunts of thieves in order to give information for the reward

Seven-pence, to stand, to suffer seven years transportation

Sew up the sees, to give a person two black eyes

Scandal broth, tea

Scamp foot, a street robber

Scent box, the nose

School butter, whipping

Scot, a savage person

Scotch fiddle, itch

Scottish, savage, wild, chagrined

Score, a debt, fine

Scout, a watchman or beadle

Screwbado, a dirty fellow, insignificant

Scroof, to go about living with friends at their expense

Scran, victuals

Scrap, a villainous scheme

Screw, a miser

Screw loose, a quarrel between two individuals, something wrong in a man's affairs

Screen, a pound note

Sharps, persons ready to take you in on all occasions

Shake a toe, to dance

Shark, a lawyer

Shade, nice to a, very particular

She lion, a shilling

Shell, to contribute, club

Sherry, run away, be gone

Sheriff's bail, an execution

Shindy, a regular row, a general quarrel

Shiners, guineas

Shirk, to cut, to skulk

Shop, a gaol

Shop lobber, a dressed up silly coxcomb of a shopman, a powdered fop

Shopped, imprisoned

Shoot, to go skulking about

Shooting the cat, vomiting

Shove, crowd, push

Shove the tumbler, whipped at the cart's tail

Shove in the mouth, a glass of gin

Shoving the moon, moving goods by moonlight

Shoulder knot, a bailiff

Shuffle, go, morriss, begone

Slum, gammon, sham

Shy cock, a person afraid of a bailiff

Sigster, a nap, after dinner, a short sleep

Sidle, come close to

Sighers, *See* Groaners

Sight, take a, a manner of expressing contempt or ridicule by putting the thumb to the nose, with the fingers straight up in the air

Sight, a lot, a great many, a great deal

Sinkers, old stockings that have sunk the small parts into the heel

Sipper, a tea spoon

Six and eight pence, a lawyer

Sink hole, the throat

Skewer, a sword

Skin, a purse

Skinners, villains who steal children; kidnappers who entrap unwary men to enlist for soldiers

Sky parlour, a garret, or first floor next the sky

Slang, flash language, patter

Slanged, ironed on one leg

Slap bang, victuals sold at a cook shop

Slate, a sheet

Sling tale and galena, fowl and pickled pork

Slipped cove, got away

Slogg, to thump hard

Slogger, a miller, a boxer

Sluicery, a gin shop

Sluiced their gobs, drank heartily

Sluice, wet, moisten

Slubber, a heavy stupid fellow

Sly, contraband

Smack the bit, share the booty

Smart blunt, forfeit money

Smart, regular, up, awake

Smashing cove, housebreaker

Smash, to break, strike, also bad coin

Smash, a thigh of mutton and, leg of mutton, turnips, and capers

Smasher, passer of bad money

Smell, half a guinea

Smell a rat, to surmise something

Smeller, the nose

Smiter, the arm

Smicket, a shift

Smug, steal, nibble

Shaffle, highwayman

Sneak, on the morning, sneaking down in the kitchen, &c., just as the servants are up, and purloining any small articles, commonly practised by cadgers

Sneezer, the nose

Snitch, to turn, to nose, to tell tales, to turn sneak

Snorter, the nose

Snooze, to sleep, doze

Snoozing ken, a sleeping room

Snow ball, a black man

Snuffle, the nose

Snuge, thief under a bed

Solomon, the mass

Some tune, a large amount

Something short, a glass of liquor

Soul driver, methodist parson

South sea mountain, gin

Speck, a bad, a bad undertaking

Specks, barnacles, spectacles

Spicer, footpad, robber

Spicer, high, highwayman

Spike hotel, the Fleet, or King's Bench

Spilt, overturned in a carriage

Spittleonian, yellow handkerchief

Spoke with, to rob

Spoke to, he's taken by the officers, cast for death

Spooney, a foolish fellow

Spoil, to bruise, injure

Spree, a lark, fun

Spurs, diggers

Spunge, to eat and drink at another's expense

Squail, a dram

Squeaker, a cross child, also a pot boy

Squeezer, a drop at Newgate

Stach, to conceal a robbery

Stool, help, assistance

Staller, an accomplice in picking of pockets by holding up the arms of persons

Stam fish, to cant

Stand the racket, treat, pay for all

Stand the nonsense, pay the money, stand treat

Stand still, a table

Stale whimper, a bastard

Stall, to make a stand, to crowd

Stag, an accomplice who has turned king's evidence

Stagged, discovered

Staller, an accomplice

Stalling ken, broker's shop, or that of a person receiving stolen goods

Stampers, feet, shoes, stairs

Stark naked, gin

Star-gazers, prostitutes who frequent hedge rows

Stephen, money

Stern, the, the goat, behind, what we sit upon

Stifle a squeaker, to murder a child

Sticks, goods, chattels

Stiffner, a letter

Stick fans, gloves

Sticks, pistols

Stone pitcher, Newgate

Stoop, the pillory

Stow it, drop it, be quiet

Stow your whid, be silent

Stranger, a guinea

Strap, mallet, trust

Strammel, straw

Stretching, hanging

Straw chipper, a straw bonnet maker

Strike, a guinea

Strings of onions, the lower orders of society

String, to, to impose on a person's belief by some joke or lie

Strike me dead, small beer

Strummer faker, hair dresser

Stumps, the feet or legs

Sucked, devilish drunk

Suit of cover me properly, suit of fashionable clothes

Sugar, cock your leg and cry, a way of expressing triumph or joy, by standing on one leg, and shaking the other up hooting 'sugar' loudly

Sufferer, a sovereign, also a tailor

Swaddy, a lobster, soldier

Swaddler, a pitiful fellow, a methodist preacher who preaches on the high road, when a number of people are assembled, his accomplices pick their pockets

Swag, a lot, much

Swallow, the throat

Swankey swipes, table beer

Sweeteners, guinea droppers

Swell out of luck, a decayed fop or dandy

Swinger, one leg and a, a sound leg and a lame one

Swig, liquor of any kind

Swigs men, thieves who travel the country under colour of buying old clothes

Swindling gloak, a cheat

T.

TACKLE, good clothes, also a mistress

Tag rag and bobtail, extremes of low life

Tail, a sword

Tallymen, persons who let out clothes to saloon cyprians

Tamarhoo, a hackney coachman, so called from the song of 'Tamarhoo; or The Devil and the Hackney Coachman'

Tanner, sixpence

Tape, gin

Tat, rum, good dice

Tatt, queer, bad dice

Tatt men, fellows who get their living by attending the gaming tables and playing at dice

Tater trap, the mummer, mouth

Tatty tog, a gaming cloth

Tattler, watch or clock

Tea-pot, a negro

Teaser, sixpence

Teazer of catgut, a fiddler

Tears of the tankard, drops of liquor

Teaze, to whip at the cart's tail

That's the ticket, just the thing as it ought to be

That dab's in quod, the rogue's in prison

Thimble, a watch

Three sheets in the wind, three parts drunk

Throw the hatchet, to, to tell a marvellous story, or a lie, and swear it's true

Thums, three pence

Tie, equal

Tib of the buttery, goose

Tibby, one on your, I owe you one

Ticker, a watch

Tidy, pretty good

Timber, matches

Timber merchant, a match dealer

Time o' day, quite right, the thing

Tinker, sixpence

Tip, money

Tip, to give

Tip your rags a gallop, to bolt, run away

Tip street, to be in, to have plenty of money

Tippy, the, just the thing, as it ought to be

Tip top, the highest, best

Tits, horses

Title-page, the face

Tizzy, sixpence

To nab a kid, to steal a child

To sing small, to draw the horns in, to be humbled

To mill a cheating bleat, to kill a sheep

To diamond a horse, to put a stone under the shoe to make it appear lame

Toddle, to walk

Toddlers, legs

Tog and kicks, breeches and coat

Togged, dressed

Togman, a cloak

Togs, clothes

Tol lol, pretty well in health

Tolo bon rig, persons who go about the country telling fortunes by signs, pretending to be deaf and dumb

Tolobon, the tongue

Tombstones, teeth

Tonic, a halfpenny

Tooth pickers, Irish watchmen's shillalies

Topper, a hat

Topping, hanging

Topping cove, hangman

Touted, to be followed, or pursued

Touch, to arrest

Tout, to look out sharp, to guard

Tow street, in, said of a person who is being misled or decoyed

Towe, clipt money

Town toddlers, silly fellows taken in by sharpers at play

Town tabby, a dowager of quality

Track, to go

Traps, constables or thief takers

Transporter, the mouth

Tramp, to wander as a beggar

Translators, sellers of old boots and shoes

Trib, a prison

Trine, to hang

Trine, the new drop

Trotters, the legs

Trooper, a blowing, prostitute

Trooper, half a crown

Trump, a good one, a jolly fellow

Trulls, the lowest order of prostitutes, followers of soldiers

Truck, stealing money under pretence of changing

Tuck, victuals

Tuck out, a good meal, a bellyfull

Tuck up fair, Newgate at a hanging time

Tucked up, hanged; married

Tumbler, a cart

Turn-up, a casual set-to, a fight

Tulips of the goes, the highest order of fashionables

Tarter, a queer customer, a powerful enemy

Turnip, a watch

Turkey merchant, driver of turkeys

Twelver, a shilling

Twaddlers, pease

Twig, to see, observe

Twinklers, the eyes

Twirlers, hawkers of men's and women's clothes

Twittoe, two

Tykes, dogs

Tyke boys, dog owners

Tyro, a yokel, a novitiate

U.

UNDER the screw, in prison

Under the rose, on the sly, concealed enjoyment

Unload pewter, drinking beer from pewter pots

Unrigged, stripped of money and clothes

Up, acquainted with the conversation of the company, apprised of any transaction

Up to slum, humbug or gammon

Up the spout, articles at the pawnbrokers

Up the flue, being in trouble, on the pot

Upper Benjamin, an upper coat

Upright, alehouse pots

V.

VAMP, to pledge any article

Vampers, stockings

Vhite, gin

Velvet, the tongue

Velvet, to tip the, to talk to a woman, to impose by flowery language

Victualling office, the stomach or paunch

Voil, town

W.

WAPSTRAW, Johnny Raw, a yokel, a countryman

Wall flowers, old clothes exposed for sale

Wall it, chalking a reckoning up at a public house

Wall fruit, kissing against a wall

Warm, rich

Wattles, the ears

Water pads, fellows who rob ships

Water-heaped, a snivelling fellow

Wearing the breeches, the wife ruling the husband

Wedge, silver plate

Wet the other eye, take another glass

Wetting the neck, drinking

Whacks, shares of booty

Wheadle, a sharper

White wood, silver

White port, gin

Whither, silver bowl

Whimpshire, Yorkshire

Whiddler, a talkative fellow, an informer

Whirligig, the pillory

Whistling shop, a public house in a prison

Whisker, a bouncing lie

White buzmen, pickpockets

White toppers, white hats

White tape, gin

Whites, counterfeit silver

Wiggen, the neck

Win, a penny

Wipe, fogle, handkerchief

Wing, fly, up, acquainted with

Wobble, to reel, drunk

Wo ball, a milk woman

Wood pecker, a punster, joker, player on words

Wooden ruff, the pillory, as he wore the wooden ruff, he stood in the pillory

W's, between the two, hitting in the belly between wind and water

Won't suit, no go, it won't do

Y.

YACE and onions, watch and seal

Yam, to eat hearty

Yankee, a tawney man

Yard of tape, a glass of gin

Yarmouth capon, a red herring

Yarum, food made of milk

Yellow boys, goldfinches, sovereigns

Yellowman, a yellow handkerchief

Yelper, a fellow who makes pitiful lamentations of trifles

Yokels, green horns, countrymen

THE SIXTY ORDERS OF
PRIME COVES.

1. Rum-bubbers
2. Coves
3. Groaners
4. Duffers
5. Out-and-outers
6. Coiners
7. Macers
8. Swigs men
9. Bully rocks
10. Lully priggers
11. Ginglers
12. Ken coves
13. Bully huffs
14. Starrers
15. Strollers
16. Mounters
17. Shoplifters
18. Swadlers
19. Sweeteners
20. Clapper dogens
21. Cloak twitchers
22. Upright men
23. Dubs men
24. Forkers
25. Bullies

26. Autem men

27. Beau nappers

28. Badgers

29. Cadgers

30. Beau traps

31. Twirlers

32. Gammoners

33. Groaners

34. Fencers

35. Spicers

36. High topers

37. Footpads

38. Gamblers

39. Swindlers

40. Shoplifters

41. Sturdy beggars

42. Pad priggers

43. Money lenders

44. Ken crackers

45. Queer culls

46. Rushers

47. Fawney coves

48. Divers

49. Adam iglers

50. Knackers

51. Millers

52. Smashers

53. Filers

54. Gypsies

55.   Buffers

56.   Priggers

57.   Rum padders

58.   Gaggers

59.   Dragsmen

60.   Bloods

FINIS.